Electronics II

D C Green

M Tech, CEng, MIEE

Fourth edition

Longman
Scientific &
Technical

Longman Scientific & Technical,
Longman Group UK Limited,
Longman House, Burnt Mill, Harlow,
Essex CM20 2JE, England
and Associated Companies throughout the world

First published in Great Britain by Pitman Publishing Limited 1978
Reprinted 1979, 1981, 1982
Second edition 1982
Reprinted 1983
Third edition 1985
Reprinted by Longman Scientific & Technical 1986
Fourth edition 1988
Reprinted 1989, 1990, 1992

British Library Cataloguing in Publication Data

Green, D.C. (Derek Charles), 1931–
    Electronics II. – 4th ed.
    1. Electronic equipment
    I. Title
    621.381

ISBN 0-582-01308-9

Set in Compugraphic Times

Printed in Malaysia by TCP

Contents

Preface to the Fourth Edition

The latest revision of the Business and Technician Education Council (BTEC) schemes for Electronic, Electrical, Computer and Tele-communication technicians has introduced a new electronics unit at level II. This new unit has much in common with the original unit but it also introduces several new topics. In this fourth edition of the book a complete revision has been carried out to ensure coverage of the contents of the new unit.

D.C.G.

1 Simplified Semiconductor Theory

A semiconductor is defined as a material whose resistivity is much less than the resistivity of an insulator yet is much greater than the resistivity of a conductor, *and* whose resistivity decreases with increase in temperature. For example, the resistivity of copper is 10^{-8} ohm-metre, of quartz is 10^{12} ohm-metres, and for the semiconductor materials of interest in this chapter, that of silicon is 0.5 ohm-metre and that of germanium is 2300 ohm-metres at 27°C. To gain an appreciation of the operation of semiconductors and semiconductor devices, it is necessary to have some familiarity with the basic concepts of the atomic structure of matter.

A Simple Outline of Atomic Theory

All the substances which occur in Nature consist of one or more basic elements; a substance containing more than one element is known as a compound. An **element** is a substance that can neither be decomposed (broken into a number of other substances) by ordinary chemical action, nor made by a chemical union of a number of other substances. A compound consists of two or more different elements in combination and has properties different from the properties of its constituent parts. Water, for example, is a compound of oxygen and hydrogen. A **molecule** is the smallest amount of a substance that can occur by itself and still retain the characteristic properties of that substance, and may consist, for example, of two atoms of hydrogen and two atoms of oxygen for hydrogen peroxide, of one atom of oxygen and one atom of carbon for carbon monoxide, and of two atoms of oxygen and one atom of carbon for carbon dioxide. An **atom** is the smallest unit of which a chemical element is built. The atoms of any particular element all have the same average mass and this average mass differs from the average mass of the atoms of any other element.

The elements are grouped in an arrangement known as the Periodic Table of the Elements (Table 1.1) according to their chemical properties. Elements with similar properties are placed in the same vertical column. More than 100 elements are known to

1

Table 1.1

I	II	III	IV	V	VI	VII	VIII	0
Hydrogen 1								Helium 2
Lithium 3	Beryllium 4	Boron 5	Carbon 6	Nitrogen 7	Oxygen 8	Fluorine 9		Neon 10
Sodium 11	Magnesium 12	Aluminium 13	Silicon 14	Phosphorus 15	Sulphur 16	Chlorine 17		Argon 18
Potassium 19	Calcium 20	Scandium 21	Titanium 22	Vanadium 23	Chromium 24	Manganese 25	Iron 26 Cobalt 27 Nickel 28	
Copper 29	Zinc 30	Gallium 31	Germanium 32	Arsenic 33	Selenium 34	Bromine 35		Krypton 36
Rubidium 37	Strontium 38	Yttrium 39	Zirconium 40	Niobium 41	Molybdenum 42	Technetium 43	Ruthenium 44 Rhodium 45 Palladium 46	
Silver 47	Cadmium 48	Indium 49	Tin 50	Antimony 51	Tellurium 52	Iron 53		Xenon 54
Caesium 55	Barium 56	Rare Earths 57–71	Hafnium 72	Tantalum 73	Tungsten 74	Rhenium 75	Osmium 76 Iridium 77 Platinum 78	
Gold 79	Mercury 80	Thallium 81	Lead 82	Bismuth 83	Polonium 84	Astatine 85		Radon 86
Francium 87	Radium 88	Actinide Series 89–100						

science today; some of them exist in large quantities and are commonly found throughout the world, e.g. oxygen, hydrogen and carbon, while others such as gold, uranium and radium are relatively rare, and some do not naturally occur on earth and are artificially created in equipment operated by atomic physicists.

An atom of any element consists of a complex pattern of electrons and a positively charged nucleus. The electrons are assumed to follow various orbits around the nucleus. The **electrons** each have a negative charge of 1.602×10^{-19} coulomb (known as the electronic charge e) and exist in just sufficient number to make the overall electrical charge of the atom equal to zero. The **nucleus** itself consists of a certain number A of particles known as nucleons. A is the mass number of the atom. There are two kinds of nucleons: **protons**, which each have a positive charge of e coulomb and **neutrons**, which have zero charge. The number of protons in a nucleus is known as the atomic number of the atom, symbol Z, and the number of neutrons the neutron number N.

Hence $A = Z + N$.

The difference between the atoms of the various elements is in the number and arrangement of the electrons, protons and neutrons of which the atoms are composed. There is no difference between an electron in one element and another electron in any other element.

The Hydrogen Atom

The simplest atom is that of the element hydrogen and it consists merely of a single proton in the nucleus and a single electron in orbit around it (Fig. 1.1a). The helium atom is the next simplest and can be seen from Fig. 1.1b to consist of a nucleus (containing two protons and two neutrons) with two electrons orbiting around it.

For an electron to be able to move in a circular path around a nucleus, as shown in Fig. 1.1, it must have a force exerted on it pulling it towards the nucleus. This force is the electrical attractive force

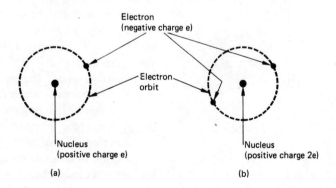

Fig. 1.1 The hydrogen and helium atoms

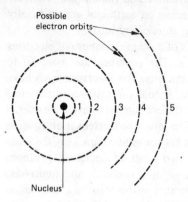

Possible electron orbits

Nucleus

Fig. 1.2 Possible electron orbits in a hydrogen atom

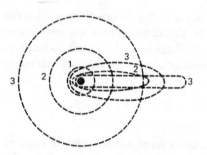

Fig. 1.3 Possible elliptical electron orbits in a hydrogen atom

exerted by the positive nucleus on the negative electron. Work must be done in moving an electric charge through an electric field and so some work must have been done to move the electron from the nucleus to the orbit in which it is travelling. Thus an electron must possess a certain, discrete, quantity of energy before it can exist in an orbit around the nucleus. An electron can only exist in certain orbits of particular radii, and when in one of these orbits it must then possess the particular amount of energy associated with that orbit. An electron cannot occupy any orbit other than one of the orbits allowed as shown in Fig. 1.2. Normally the electron travels the innermost orbit since this is the orbit of least energy, but if it is given, in some way, extra energy, such as heat, it will move to another orbit. An electron can only absorb the exact amount of energy required to raise its total energy to the energy value associated with another orbit; if given this amount of energy the electron will move to its new orbit and remain there until it loses some of its energy. The electron can only lose the exact amount of energy that will allow it to fall into a lower-energy orbit. This means that an electron can only absorb or lose energy in discrete amounts.

The simplified picture of the hydrogen atom given so far cannot account for all the observed phenomena, and it is necessary to extend the model by imagining that the electron can also move in elliptical orbits (Fig. 1.3). The number of elliptical orbits possible is equal to $n - 1$, where n is the number of the basic circular orbits. The innermost orbit, $n = 1$, has no elliptical paths associated with it; the next orbit, $n = 2$, has a single elliptical path and so on. The circular orbits, numbers 1, 2, 3, etc. are said to form the K, L, M, etc. **shells**. The elliptical orbits are said to form sub-shells within these shells.

Other Atoms

The extra-nuclear make-up of the other, more complex, elements can be deduced with accuracy up to the element of atomic number 18 (argon), by adding one more electron for each element in turn, bearing in mind that the number, x, of electrons permitted in a particular shell is given by the expression $x = 2n^2$, where n is the order of the shell. The innermost shell can only contain 2×1^2 or 2 electrons, the next shell 2×2^2 or 8 electrons, the next 2×3^2 or 18 electrons, and so on. The electrons in a particular shell follow paths of different eccentricities. Above atomic number 18 some gaps appear in this system because some orbits in the N shell have lower energy than some orbits in the M shell and are filled first.

The Periodic Table of the Elements is given in Table 1.1.

The atoms of all elements in group III have three electrons that are not part of a closed shell or sub-shell. Aluminium, for example, has 13 electrons, 10 of which completely fill the K and L shells; the M shell has only three electrons and is incomplete (since 18 electrons are necessary to fill it).

Indium is also in group III and has 49 electrons, 28 of which complete the K, L and M shells. Of the remaining 21 electrons, 18 completely fill three of the four sub-shells of the N shell and the remaining three enter the O shell (leaving the fourth sub-shell of the N shell unfilled). For both aluminium and indium, therefore, the extra-nuclear structure consists of a number of tightly bound closed shells and sub-shells with three electrons outside and not so tightly bound to the nucleus.

The electronic structure of all the other atoms is also in the form of a number of closed shells and sub-shells with a number of electrons in orbit outside. The nucleus of an atom plus the closed shells and sub-shells of electrons can be considered to be a positively charged central core, the positive charge being equal to $e \times n$, where e is the electronic charge and n is the number of electrons outside the central core. The number of electrons outside this central core is equal to the number of the group in the Periodic Table of the Elements to which the atom belongs. Thus all atoms in group I may be represented by the sketch of Fig. 1.4a, all atoms in group II by Fig. 1.4b, and so on.

The outer electrons are known as valence electrons and determine the chemical properties of the element.

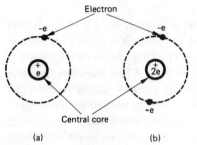

Fig. 1.4 Representation of (a) group I atoms and (b) group II atoms

Intrinsic Semiconductors

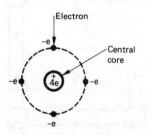

Fig. 1.5 Representation of germanium or silicon atom

The two semiconductor materials used in the manufacture of semiconductor devices, such as diodes and transistors, are germanium and silicon. It can be seen from Table 1.1 that both these materials fall into group IV of the Periodic Table of the Elements. An atom of either substance may be represented by a central core of positive charge $4e$ surrounded by four orbiting electrons each of which has a negative charge of e (Fig. 1.5). In the remainder of this chapter the discussion of semiconductors will be with reference to silicon but will apply equally well to germanium; any differences between the two materials will be mentioned in the appropriate places. In its solid state, silicon forms crystals of the diamond type, that is it forms a cubic lattice in which all the atoms (except those at the surface) are equidistant from their immediately neighbouring atoms. A study of crystal structures shows that the greatest number of atoms that can be neighbours to a particular atom at an equal distance away from that atom and yet be equidistant from one another is four. Hence each atom in a silicon crystal has four neighbouring atoms. In the crystal lattice each atom employs its four valence electrons to form **covalent bonds** with its four neighbouring atoms; each bond consisting of two electrons, one from each atom as shown in Fig. 1.6a. Each pair of electrons traverses an orbit around both its parent atom and a neighbouring atom. Each atom is effectively provided with an extra four electrons and these are sufficient to complete its final sub-shell. To simplify the drawings in the remainder of this chapter, covalent bonding will be represented in the manner of Fig. 1.6b.

If the temperature of the crystal is raised above absolute zero the lattice is thermally excited and some of the valence electrons receive sufficient energy to break free from a covalent bond. When this occurs the liberated electrons wander randomly in the crystal and are free to accept further energy from an applied electric field and contribute to electrical conduction. With further increase in temperature more covalent bonds are broken, and the conductivity of the silicon is increased because of the increased number of free electrons. This means that a semiconductor material has a negative temperature coefficient of resistance.

When an electron escapes from a covalent bond it leaves behind it an 'absence of an electron' which, since it consists of a missing negative charge e, is equivalent to a positive charge of magnitude e. Such a positive charge is known as a **hole**. A hole exerts an attractive force on electrons and can be filled by a nearby passing electron that has been previously liberated from another broken covalent bond. This process is known as recombination and it causes a continual loss of holes and free electrons. At any given temperature the rate of recombination of holes and electrons is always equal to the rate of production of new holes and electrons so that the total number of free electrons and holes is constant.

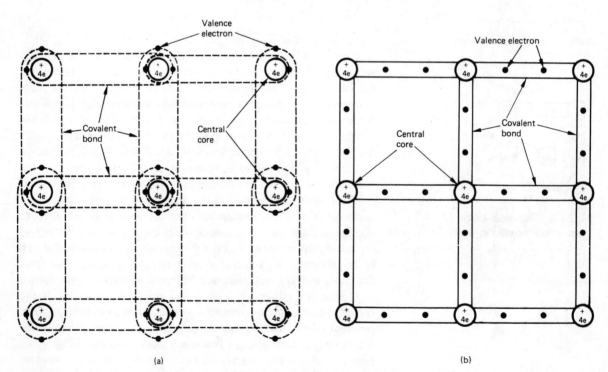

(a)   (b)

Fig. 1.6 Covalent bonding of atoms

When a covalent bond is broken it is said that a **hole-electron pair** has been created; both holes and electrons are known as **charge carriers**. The lifetime of a charge carrier is the time that elapses between its creation and its recombination with a charge carrier of opposite sign.

Movement of Holes through the Lattice

Fig. 1.7 shows a part of a silicon crystal in which the breaking of covalent bonds by thermal agitation of the lattice is taking place. In Fig. 1.7a thermal agitation of the crystal lattice has caused a covalent bond to break and produce a hole-electron pair at point A.

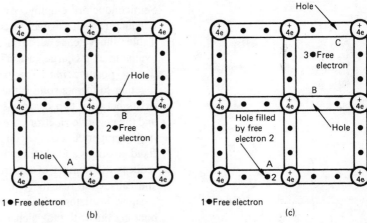

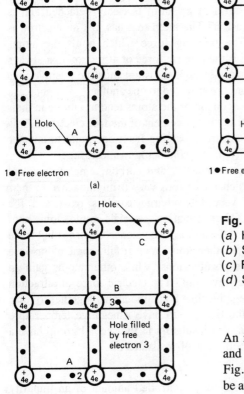

Fig. 1.7 The movement of holes through a crystal lattice
(a) Hole-electron pair created
(b) Second hole-electron pair created
(c) First hole disappeared and third hole-electron pair created
(d) Second hole disappeared

An instant later a second hole-electron pair is produced at point B and two electrons are free to wander in the lattice (Fig. 1.7b). In Fig. 1.7c electron 2 has wandered close enough to the first hole to be attracted by its electric field and recombination has occurred. The original hole has apparently moved from position A to position B, but at the same time another hole-electron pair has been created at point C. Finally, in Fig. 1.7d, free electron 3 has travelled across the lattice and has recombined with the hole at point B and the effect is as though a hole has moved through the lattice from point A to point C.

The movement of both holes and electrons through the crystal is quite random but the holes appear to travel more slowly than do electrons. (This is because the movement of a hole in a particular direction actually consists of a series of discontinuous electron movements in the opposite direction.) If an electric field is set up in the crystal the holes tend to *drift* in the direction of the field and the electrons to *drift* in the opposite direction. Thus conduction of current in a pure semiconductor, known as intrinsic conduction, takes place (current flow is conventionally in the opposite direction to electron flow). Intrinsic conduction increases with increase in temperature at the approximate rate of 5% per degree Centigrade for germanium and 7% per °C for silicon.

Conductors and Insulators

A material acts as a conductor, an insulator, or a semiconductor as a consequence of the way in which its atoms are bound together. Semiconductors employ covalent bonding as just explained. In a conductor, such as silver or copper, that is in group I of the Periodic Table, the valence electron of an atom is easily detached and is available as a charge carrier. The atom that has lost an electron is then a positive *ion*. The bonding force which holds the atoms together to form a solid is the electric force of attraction that always exists between two charges of opposite sign; thus the positive ions and the negative electrons are attracted to one another. With increase in the temperature of the conductor the atoms tend to vibrate in their fixed positions and obstruct the movement of the free electrons. This reduces the number of electrons passing from one point to another and causes the resistivity of the conductor to increase.

Some insulators, such as plastics and carbon, employ covalent bonding but with the valence electrons very firmly attached to their parent atoms. Hence very few charge carriers exist and the resistivity is very high. Other insulating materials employ ionic bonding; in this case some of the atoms lose valence electrons but these move into orbit around another atom. As a result, some atoms lose an electron and become positive ions, while other atoms gain an electron and become negative ions. The electric force of attraction between positive and negative ions holds the atoms together to form a solid. Insulators in the first group have a negative temperature coefficient of resistance, and insulators in the second group have a positive temperature coefficient of resistance.

Extrinsic (Impurity) Semiconductors

If an extremely small, carefully controlled amount of an impurity element is introduced into a silicon crystal, each of the impurity atoms will take the place of one of the silicon atoms in the lattice. Since the number of impurity atoms is very much smaller than the number of silicon atoms (approximately 1 in 10^8), it is reasonable to assume that the lattice is essentially undisturbed and that each impurity atom is surrounded by four silicon atoms. In practice, the impurities are always substances in either group III or group V of

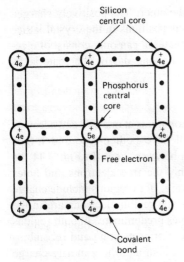

Fig. 1.8 Lattice of n-type silicon crystal

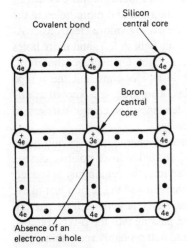

Fig. 1.9 Lattice of p-type silicon crystal

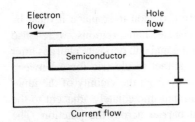

Fig. 1.10 Current flow in an extrinsic semiconductor

the Periodic Table of the Elements, and have either three or five valence electrons. Elements typically employed are arsenic, antimony and phosphorus in group V, and indium, aluminium and gallium in group III. The process of introducing impurity atoms into a silicon crystal is called **'doping'** and a treated crystal is said to be 'doped'.

n-type Semiconductor

Suppose a silicon crystal has been doped with a small quantity of phosphorus, a substance having five valence electrons. Each phosphorus atom will set up covalent bonds with its four neighbouring atoms but, since only four of its valence electrons are required for this purpose, a spare electron exists (Fig. 1.8). This surplus electron is not bound to its parent atom and is free to wander in the lattice.

A free electron is created in the silicon crystal lattice for each impurity atom introduced without the creation of corresponding holes. Hole-electron pairs are, however, still produced by thermal agitation of the lattice. The number of free electrons in the crystal is much greater than the number of holes, negative charges predominate and so the crystal is said to be **n-type**. Since each impurity atom donates a free electron to the crystal, the impurity atoms are known as **donor** atoms.

p-type Semiconductor

If, instead of phosphorus, a group III element such as boron is introduced into a silicon crystal, each boron atom will attempt to form a covalent bond with each of its four neighbouring silicon atoms. Boron, however, has only three valence electrons and so only three of the bonds can be completed (Fig. 1.9). One hole is introduced into the lattice for each impurity atom and is able to move about in the crystal in the same way as a hole produced by thermal agitation. In this case holes are in the majority and the material is known as **p-type**, while the impurity atoms are called **acceptor** atoms.

A crystal of n-type or p-type silicon is electrically neutral because each impurity atom introduced into the lattice is itself neutral. In n-type material, electrons are the **majority charge carriers** and holes are the **minority charge carriers**. In p-type material the electrons are the minority charge carriers and holes are the majority charge carriers.

Current Flow

If a potential difference is maintained across an extrinsic semiconductor (Fig. 1.10), a drift current will flow into the material at one end and out of the material at the other. The positively charged central cores cannot move from their positions in the crystal lattice and so the current flowing *into* the material can only consist of electrons flowing *out* and the current flowing *out* of the material is actually an inward flow of electrons.

The p-n Junction

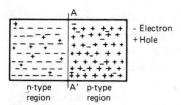

- Electron
+ Hole

n-type region   A'   p-type region

Fig. 1.11 The formation of a p-n junction

If a silicon crystal is doped with donor atoms at one end and acceptor atoms at the other the crystal will have both p-type and n-type regions and there will be a junction between them. In Fig. 1.11 the plane AA′ is the **p-n junction**; only the free electrons and holes have been shown to clarify the drawing. Both regions include charge carriers of either sign but in the n-type region electrons are in the majority and in the p-type region holes predominate. In both regions the probability of a minority charge carrier meeting and recombining with a majority charge carrier is high and the minority charge carrier lifetime is short.

The free electrons and holes have completely random motions and wander freely in the lattice. However, since there are more electrons to the left of the p-n junction than to the right and more holes to the right of the junction than to the left, *on average* more electrons cross the junction from left to right than from right to left, and more holes cross from right to left than from left to right. On average, therefore, the n-type region gains holes and loses electrons and the p-type region gains electrons and loses holes. This process is known as **diffusion** and may be defined as the tendency for charge carriers to move away from areas of high density.

Since the n-type region loses negative charge carriers and gains positive charge carriers, and the p-type region loses positive charge carriers and gains negative charge carriers, the region just to the left of the junction becomes positively charged and the region just to the right of the junction becomes negatively charged. A hole passing into the n-type region, or an electron passing into the p-type region, becomes a minority charge carrier and will probably recombine with a carrier of opposite sign and disappear; however, one region has still lost a positive (or negative) charge and the other region has gained a negative (or positive) charge. The movement of holes and electrons across the junction constitutes a current and this is known as the **diffusion current**.

If the crystal was neutral before diffusion took place it must be neutral afterwards. Further, because both regions were also originally neutral they must contain equal and opposite charges after diffusion. These charges have an attractive electric force between them and are not able to diffuse away from the vicinity of the junction. The two charges are concentrated immediately adjacent to the junction, and produce a potential barrier across the junction. The polarity of the potential barrier is such as to oppose the further diffusion of majority charge carriers across the junction, but to aid the

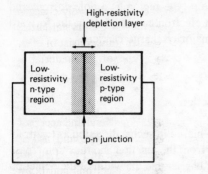

Fig. 1.12 The unbiased p-n junction

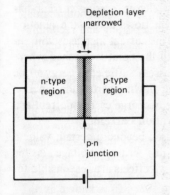

Fig. 1.13 The forward-biased p-n junction

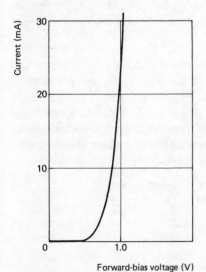

Fig. 1.14 The current/voltage characteristic of a forward biased p-n junction

movement of minority charge carriers; this gives rise to a minority charge carrier current in the opposite direction to the diffusion current.

The difference in potential from one side of the junction to the other is called the *height of the potential barrier* and is measured in volts. The height of the potential barrier attains such a value that the majority charge carrier (diffusion) and minority charge carrier currents are equal and so the net current across the junction is zero. Any charge carriers entering the region on either side of the junction over which the barrier potential is effective are rapidly swept out of it, and hence this region is depleted of charge carriers.

The **depletion layer**, as it is called, is a region of relatively high resistivity and is approximately 0.001 mm in width.

If an external source of e.m.f. is applied across the p-n junction, the equilibrium state of the junction is disturbed and the potential barrier is either increased or decreased according to the polarity of the external e.m.f. The silicon crystal consists of two regions of low resistivity separated by a region of high resistivity, the depletion layer (see Fig. 1.12), and the application of an e.m.f. across the crystal is effectively the same as placing it across the depletion layer.

The Forward-biased p-n Junction

If a battery is connected across the crystal in the direction shown in Fig. 1.13, holes are repelled from the positive end of the crystal and are caused to drift towards the junction; and electrons are repelled from the negative end of the crystal and also drift towards the junction. This drift of holes and electrons towards the junction reduces both the width of the depletion layer and the height of the potential barrier, and the junction is said to be **forward biased**. The reduction in the height of the potential barrier allows majority charge carriers of lower energy to cross the junction and, since the minority charge carrier current remains constant, there is a net majority charge carrier current across the junction from the p-type region to the n-type region. This current increases very rapidly with increase in the forward bias voltage as can be seen from the typical current/voltage characteristic shown in Fig. 1.14.

The holes drifting through the p-type region towards the p-n junction may be considered to have been injected by the positive terminal of the battery. Some of these holes may recombine with electrons diffusing across the junction in the other direction and so the hole current across the junction is slightly less than the injected hole current. After they have passed across the junction the holes recombine with the excess electrons in the n-type region. Similarly, the negative battery terminal injects electrons into the n-type region and most of these electrons cross the junction. The total current is the sum of the electron and hole currents and is constant throughout the crystal. The current enters the p-type region as a hole current and leaves the n-type region as an electron current, i.e. in the forward direction current flow is by majority charge carriers.

The Reverse-biased p-n Junction

Fig. 1.15 shows a p-n junction biased in such a direction as to attract majority charge carriers away from the junction and thus to increase both the height of the potential barrier and the width of the depletion layer. Fewer majority charge carriers now have sufficient energy to be able to surmount the potential barrier and the majority charge carrier current decreases. The minority charge carrier current has remained constant and so a net current flows across the junction from n-type region to p-type region. This current increases with increase in the reverse bias voltage until the point is reached where almost no majority charge carriers possess sufficient energy to be able to cross the junction. The current flowing across the junction is then constant and equal to the minority charge carrier current and it is then known as the **reverse saturation current**.

If the reverse bias voltage is increased beyond a certain value a rapid increase in current occurs; this critical voltage is the **breakdown voltage** of the junction. Two effects are responsible for breakdown:

  (a) the **Zener effect** in which the electric field across the junction is strong enough to break some of the covalent bonds and
  (b) the **avalanche effect** in which charge carriers are accelerated to such an extent that they are able to break covalent bonds by collision.

A typical current/voltage characteristic for a reverse-biased p-n junction is shown in Fig. 1.16. If the temperature of a p-n junction is increased the number of minority charge carriers generated and able to cross the junction will also increase. This will increase the reverse saturation current. Manufacturers of semiconductor devices recommend maximum junction temperatures which should not be exceeded. For most devices these limits are:

germanium 90°C silicon 150°C (plastic case)
200°C (metal case)

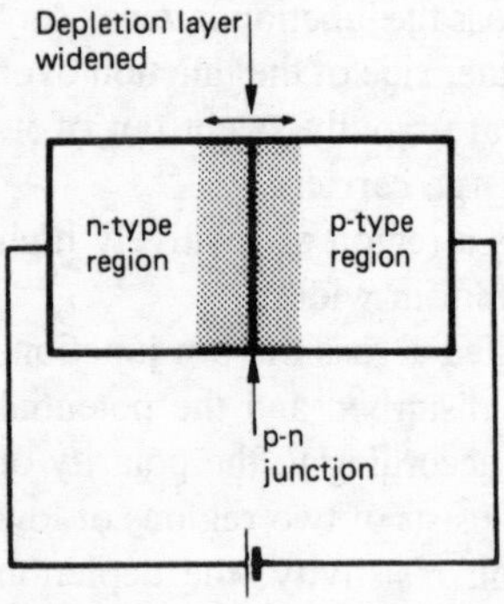

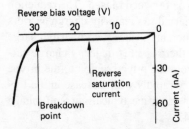

Fig. 1.15 The reverse-biased p-n junction

Fig. 1.16 The current/voltage characteristic of a reverse-biased p-n junction

The Capacitance of a p-n Junction

When a p-n junction is reverse-biased, the depletion layer is a high-resistance region with low-resistance regions either side and so it acts as though it were a parallel-plate capacitor, the capacitance of which is a function of the magnitude of the applied bias voltage. A p-n junction can be made with the transition from the p-type region to the n-type region either abrupt or gradual. For an abrupt junction the depletion capacitance is proportional to the square root of the bias voltage, and for a gradual junction, to the cube root.

2 Semiconductor Diodes

Construction

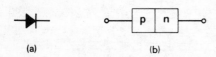

(a)   (b)

Fig. 2.1 The basic semiconductor diode

The semiconductor diode is a device that has a high resistance to the flow of current in one direction and a low resistance in the other. The diode is widely employed in electronic circuitry for many different purposes and it consists essentially of a p-n junction formed in either a silicon or a germanium crystal (Fig. 2.1b). The symbol for a semiconductor diode is shown in Fig. 2.1a. The direction in which the diode offers little opposition to current flow is indicated by the arrowhead.

Germanium and silicon for use in the manufacture of semiconductor diodes must be first purified until an impurity concentration of less than 1 part in 10^{10} is achieved. The wanted impurity atoms, donors and/or acceptors, are then added in the required amounts and the material is made into a single crystal.

A p-n junction may be formed in a number of different ways but two basic techniques are generally employed, either singly or in combination. An example of the first method is outlined in Fig. 2.2 and consists of alloying an indium pellet on to an n-type germanium wafer.

To make the n-type germanium wafer some intrinsic germanium and a small amount of impurity are melted in a crucible in a vacuum, and a seed crystal is lowered into the melt to a depth of a few millimetres. The temperature of the molten germanium is just above the melting point of the seed crystal, and the few millimetres of seed immersed in the melt also melt. The seed is rotated at a constant velocity and at the same time is slowly withdrawn from the melt, thus forming an n-type crystal. By careful control of the process the required impurity concentration can be achieved.

A pellet of indium is placed on the germanium wafer and is heated to a temperature above the melting point of indium but below the melting point of germanium. The indium melts and dissolves the germanium until a saturated solution of germanium in indium is obtained. The wafer is then slowly cooled and in the cooling a region of p-type germanium is produced in the wafer, and an alloy of germanium and indium (mainly indium) is deposited on the wafer. A

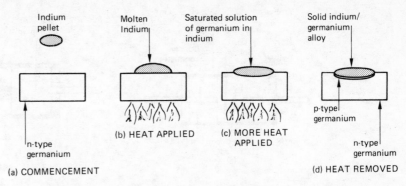

Fig. 2.2 The "alloying" method of forming a p-n junction

silicon alloyed p-n junction can be formed using the same method but with aluminium as the acceptor element.

The second method of producing a p-n junction to be considered here is diffusion and it is outlined in Fig. 2.3. The p-type germanium is heated to a temperature very nearly equal to the melting point of germanium, and is surrounded by the donor element antimony in gaseous form. The antimony atoms will diffuse into the germanium to produce an n-type region. If an n-type germanium crystal is used gallium is employed, in gaseous form, as the acceptor element to produce a p-type region in the crystal. When a silicon device is to be manufactured, boron is used as the acceptor element and phosphorus as the donor element.

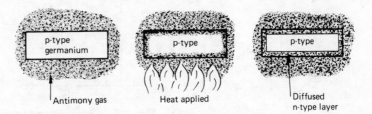

Fig. 2.3 The "diffusion" method of forming a p-n junction

A **junction diode** consists of a crystal having both p-type and n-type regions. Junction diodes are made from either germanium or silicon, the former having the advantage of a lower forward resistance and the latter the advantages of a higher breakdown voltage and a lower reverse saturation current. Connection to the junction is made by wires fixed to each of the two regions. The complete device is usually enclosed in a hermetically sealed container to prevent the entry of moisture (see Fig. 2.4a).

The silicon planar diode is manufactured using the diffusion method, and a typical construction is shown in Fig. 2.4b.

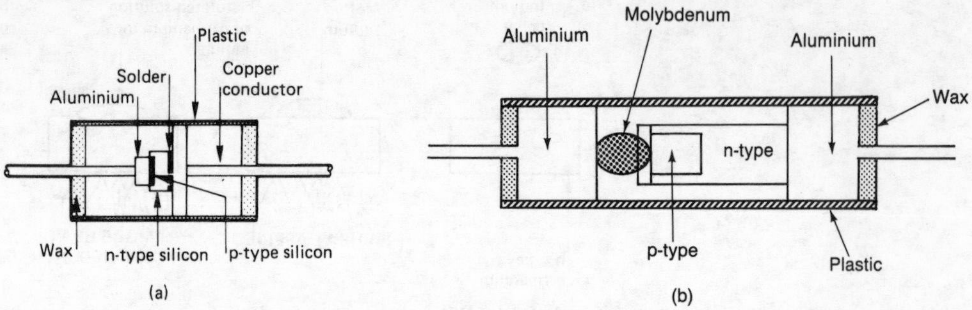

Fig. 2.4 Construction of (a) a silicon junction diode and (b) a silicon planar diode

Semiconductor Diode Current/ Voltage Characteristics

The current/voltage characteristic of a semiconductor diode is a graph of the current flowing in the device plotted against the voltage applied across it.

It can be measured with the aid of the circuit arrangement of Fig. 2.5. With the switch in the position shown, the diode is reverse-biased; to forward bias the diode, the switch is thrown to its other position in order to reverse the polarity of the applied voltage. For each position of the switch, the applied voltage is increased from zero in a number of steps and the current flowing at each step is noted. The noted current values are then plotted to a base of voltage.

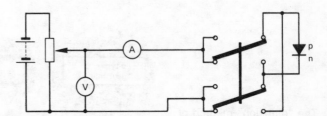

Fig. 2.5 Circuit for measuring the current/voltage characteristic of a semiconductor diode

Typical current/voltage characteristics for silicon and germanium diodes are shown in Fig. 2.6.

Note that the forward current does not increase to any noticeable extent until the forward bias voltage is greater than about 0.6 V for the silicon diode and about 0.2 V for the germanium diode. The other features of importance are (i) the reverse saturation current, and (ii) the reverse breakdown voltage (not shown). The a.c. resistance of a diode at a particular d.c. voltage is equal to the reciprocal of the slope of the characteristic at that point, that is

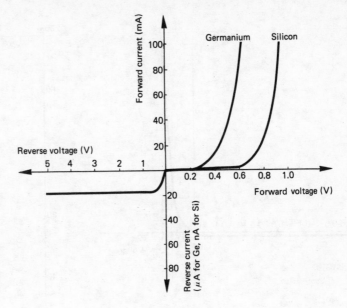

Fig. 2.6 Current/voltage characteristics for a silicon diode and a germanium diode

$$r_{ac} = \frac{\text{Change in voltage}}{\text{Resulting change in current}} = \frac{\delta V}{\delta I} \text{ ohm}$$

(*Note* The Greek letter δ (delta) means "a change of" wherever it appears in formulae. So, δt is a change of time. Generally it indicates a small-scale change.)

At any point along the characteristic the ratio (voltage applied/current flowing) is a measure of the d.c. resistance of the diode for that voltage. If the characteristic is linear this ratio will be a constant quantity but should the characteristic be non-linear, the d.c. resistance will vary with the point of measurement.

Example 2.1

Calculate the a.c. resistance of the semiconductor diode whose characteristic is shown in Fig. 2.7 at the point +1 V.

Solution

The a.c. resistance r_{ac} is equal to $\delta V/\delta I$ and to find the forward resistance at the point $V = 1$ V it is necessary to select two equidistant points either side of this voltage and then, by projection to and from the characteristic, find the corresponding values of current.

Two points 0.2 V either side of +1 V have been selected, hence $\delta V = 0.4$ V.

Projection upwards from these points to the curve and then from the curve to the current axis, as shown by the dotted lines, shows that the corresponding values of current are 15.5 mA and 5.5 mA, i.e.

$$\delta I = 10 \text{ mA} \quad r_{ac} = 0.4/10 \times 10^{-3} = 40 \text{ ohms} \quad (Ans.)$$

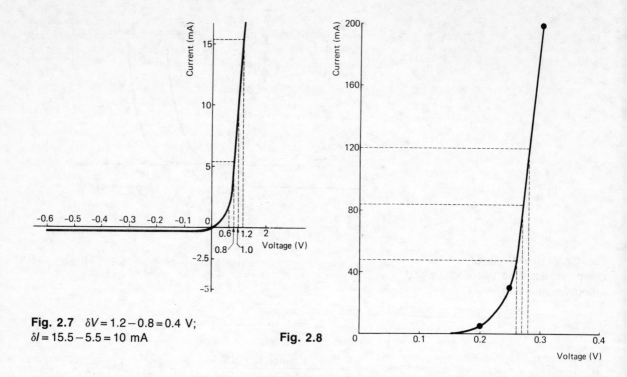

Fig. 2.7 $\delta V = 1.2 - 0.8 = 0.4$ V;
$\delta I = 15.5 - 5.5 = 10$ mA

Fig. 2.8

The slope of the reverse saturation current curve is very small and cannot be measured from the characteristic; this means that the reverse a.c. resistance of the diode is high, of the order of several thousands of ohms.

Example 2.2

The current/voltage characteristic of a semiconductor diode is given in the table.

Voltage (V)	0.05	0.10	0.15	0.20	0.25	0.30
Current (mA)	0.2	0.4	0.6	4.0	30	200

Plot the characteristic and use it to determine (i) the d.c. resistance and (ii) the a.c. resistance of the diode at the point when $V = 0.27$ volts.

Solution

The current/voltage characteristic of the diode is shown plotted in Fig. 2.8.

(i) The d.c. resistance of the diode at the point $V = 0.27$ V is found by drawing a line upwards from the voltage axis to the characteristic and then projecting on to the current axis. The corresponding d.c. current value is 84 mA and therefore

$$r_{dc} = \frac{V}{I} = \frac{0.27}{84 \times 10^{-3}} = 3.21 \ \Omega \quad (Ans.)$$

(ii) The a.c. resistance of the diode is determined using the method of the preceding example. Points 0.01 V either side of 0.27 V have been selected so that $\delta V = 0.02$ V. The corresponding current values are 120 mA and 48 mA; hence $\delta I = 72$ mA. Therefore

$$r_{ac} = \frac{\delta V}{\delta I} = \frac{0.02}{72 \times 10^{-3}} = 0.28 \ \Omega \quad (Ans.)$$

It is important that small increments of voltage are chosen when calculating r_{ac}, otherwise considerable error may occur. Suppose, for example, that points 0.03 V either side of $V = 0.27$ V had been selected. Then $\delta V = 0.06$ V and $\delta I = 178$ mA giving

$$r_{ac} = \frac{0.06}{178 \times 10^{-3}} \text{ or } 0.34 \ \Omega$$

This is a percentage error of $\dfrac{0.34 - 0.28}{0.28} \times 100$ or 21.43%

Forward Voltage Drop

When a voltage is applied across a semiconductor diode with the polarity required to forward bias its p-n junction, the barrier potential is reduced which allows more majority charge carriers to cross the junction. Since the minority charge carrier current is unaffected, a net current flows across the junction. As the forward bias voltage is increased, the current is very small at first but it increases rapidly once the voltage has exceeded a particular threshold value. For a silicon diode this **threshold voltage** is approximately 0.6 V, but it is only about 0.2 V for a germanium diode. This is clearly shown by the typical characteristics of Fig. 2.6.

Forward Current

For each type of diode, a maximum forward average current $I_{F(AV)}$ and a maximum repetitive forward current I_{FRM} are quoted by the manufacturer.

Reverse Saturation Current

When a reverse bias voltage is applied to a semiconductor diode, the barrier potential is increased and fewer majority charge carriers have sufficient energy to cross the junction. With increase in the reverse bias voltage, the point is reached where the current consists almost entirely of minority charge carriers. The current flowing then becomes more or less constant and is known as the **reverse saturation current**. The reverse saturation current in a germanium diode is very much greater than the reverse saturation current of a silicon diode of comparable maximum forward current rating. Thus, for the smaller types of diode the reverse saturation current would be a few microamperes in a germanium diode but only a few nanoamperes in a silicon diode.

If the temperature of the p-n junction is increased, further hole electron pairs will be produced and the reverse saturation current will become larger.

Breakdown Voltage

If the reverse bias voltage applied to a diode is steadily increased, the current will remain at an approximately constant value until a point is reached where a sudden and large increase in current takes place (Fig. 2.9). In the breakdown region the reverse resistance of the diode will be low. Also this large increase in current will dissipate power within the diode and may lead to the destruction of the device. It is necessary therefore, to ensure that the diode is not driven into its breakdown region. An arbitrary voltage rating is determined and quoted by the manuacturer for each type of diode which, if not exceeded, will ensure the satisfactory working of the device. The **peak inverse voltage** (p.i.v.) varies considerably with the type of diode and may easily be a few hundreds of volts.

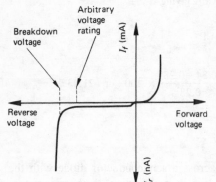

Fig. 2.9 Voltage breakdown in a semiconductor diode

Example 2.3

A silicon junction diode has the following parameters: maximum forward current 250 mA, forward voltage drop of 1.2 V at a forward current of 30 mA, a maximum reverse voltage of 50 V, and a reverse saturation current of 0.05 μA at the maximum reverse voltage.

   (i)   Sketch the current/voltage characteristic of the diode.
   (ii) Determine its d.c. resistance at a forward voltage of 1.2 V.

Solution
   (i)   The required current/voltage characteristic is given in Fig. 2.10.
   (ii) The d.c. resistance at $V = 1.2$ V is

$$r_{dc} = \frac{1.2}{0.03} = 40 \quad \Omega$$

The Semiconductor Diode as a Switch

A semiconductor diode is able to operate as a two-state device because it offers a low resistance to the flow of an electric current in one direction and a high resistance in the other. The diode is said to be ON when it is forward biased and OFF when it is reverse biased. To see how a diode acts as a two-state device consider the circuit of Fig. 2.11 which shows a diode connected in series with a load resistor R_L.

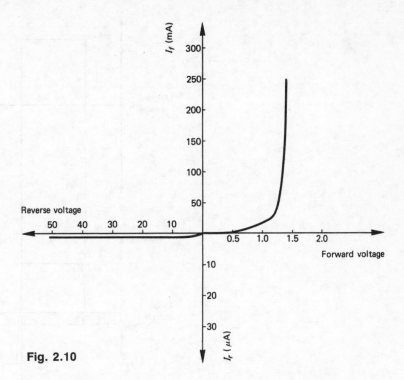

Fig. 2.10

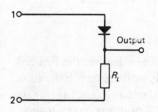

Fig. 2.11 The diode as a two-state device

Table 2.1

Terminal 1	Terminal 2	Output Terminal
Positive	Negative	Positive
Negative	Positive	Positive
Positive	Positive	Positive
Negative	Negative	Negative

When terminal 1 is positive with respect to terminal 2, the diode conducts and a current flows to develop a voltage across R_L. Neglecting the small voltage drop which must occur across the diode, the voltage appearing at the output terminals of the circuit will be equal to the voltage applied to terminal 1. When the voltage applied to terminal 2 is positive relative to the voltage at terminal 1, the diode will not conduct. The voltage at the output terminal will now be equal to the voltage at terminal 2. Suppose now that voltages of the same magnitude and polarity are applied to terminals 1 and 2. The diode will not conduct and the output voltage will be the same as the common value of the input voltages. The action of the circuit can be expressed by a *voltage table*, as Table 2.1

When a diode is employed as a switch the times it takes to switch from ON to OFF or from OFF to ON will be of importance. The time taken for a diode to turn ON is always small enough to be neglected but the turn-OFF time is larger and it provides a limiting factor to the maximum frequency at which the diode may be switched.

Fig. 2.12 shows a rectangular voltage that is applied to a diode. When the diode is forward biased the diode current flows more or less instantaneously. When the polarity of the applied voltage is reversed to turn the diode OFF, the diode does *not* immediately turn OFF, with its current falling to its reverse saturation value. Instead, the diode conducts in the reverse direction to produce an initial surge

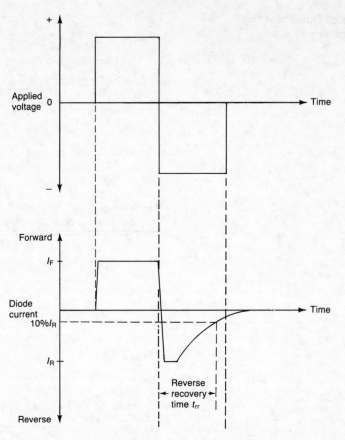

Fig. 2.12 Switching a diode

of current I_R that is equal to, or very nearly equal to, the forward current I_F. Then the reverse current falls to its reverse saturation value. The time that elapses between the diode voltage changing its polarity and the diode current reaching 10% of its maximum reverse value is known as the **reverse recovery time** t_{rr} and it is usually measured in nanoseconds.

The excess reverse current occurs because at the instant the diode voltage changes its polarity there are many charge carriers crossing the p-n junction and these must all be removed before the diode current is merely provided by the minority charge carriers.

To avoid having a surge of reverse current the reverse recovery time must be several (usually 10) times smaller than the periodic time of the applied waveform.

Example 2.4

Calculate the maximum frequency at which a diode having $t_{rr}=5$ ns can be switched.

Solution

$$T = 10 \, t_{rr} = 50 \text{ ns.}$$

Therefore $f_{max} = 1/50 \times 10^{-9} = 20$ MHz (*Ans.*)

Types of Diode and their Application

The important parameters of semiconductor diodes are

(1) Forward and reverse a.c. resistances
(2) Maximum forward current
(3) Junction capacitance
(4) Behaviour in breakdown region
(5) Reverse recovery time.

Depending upon the intended application of a diode, one or more of these parameters may be of prime importance.

The main types of diode used in modern electronic circuitry are

(1) Signal diodes (which include switching diodes)
(2) Power diodes
(3) Zener diodes
(4) Varactor diodes.

(1) Signal Diodes

The term **signal diode** includes all diodes which have been designed for use in circuits where large current and/or voltage ratings are not required. The usual requirements are for a large (reverse resistance)/ (forward resistance) ratio and minimum junction capacitance. Some of the commercially available signal diodes are listed as general-purpose types while others are best suited to a particular circuit application, e.g. as a detector of radio waves, or as an electronic switch in logic circuitry. The maximum reverse voltage, or peak inverse voltage, that the diode is likely to be called upon to handle is usually not very high, and neither is the maximum forward current. Most types of signal diode have a peak inverse voltage in the range 30 V to 150 V and a maximum forward current somewhere between 40 and 250 mA, but higher values are readily available.

(2) Power Diodes

Power diodes are most often employed for the conversion of alternating current into direct current, i.e. as rectifiers. The important power diode parameters are the peak inverse voltage, the maximum forward current, and the resistance ratio. The peak inverse voltage is likely to be somewhere between 50 V and 1000 V with a maximum forward current of perhaps 30 A. The forward resistance must be as low as possible to avoid considerable voltage drop across the diode when the large forward current flows; this resistance is usually not very much more than an ohm or two.

(3) Zener Diodes

The large reverse current which flows when the breakdown voltage of a diode is exceeded need not necessarily result in damage to the device.

A **Zener diode** is fabricated in a way which allows it to be operated in the breakdown region without damage, provided the current is restricted by external resistance to a safe value. The large current at breakdown is brought about by two factors, known as the Zener and the avalanche effects. At voltages up to about 5 V the electric field near to the junction is strong enough to pull electrons out of the covalent bonds holding the atoms together. Extra hole-electron pairs are produced and these are available to augment the reverse current. This is known as the *Zener effect*.

The *avalanche effect* occurs if the reverse bias voltage is made larger than 5 V or so. The velocity with which the charge carriers move through the crystal lattice is increased to such as extent that they attain sufficient kinetic energy to *ionize* atoms by collision. An atom is said to have been ionized when one of its electrons has been removed. The extra charge carriers thus produced travel through the crystal lattice and may also collide with other atoms to produce even more carriers by ionization. In this way the number of charge carriers, and hence the reverse current, is rapidly increased. In the forward direction a Zener diode behaves just like a silicon signal diode.

Zener diodes are available in a number of standardized *reference voltages*. For example, it is possible to obtain a Zener diode with a reference (breakdown) voltage of 8.2 V. An alternative name for the device is the *voltage reference diode*. The most common application of the Zener diode is in the voltage stabilizing circuits which are discussed in Chapter 7. It is also employed as a voltage reference. The symbol for a Zener diode is shown in Fig. 2.13.

Fig. 2.13 Zener diode symbol

Example 2.5

A Zener diode is advertised as having a breakdown voltage of 20 V with a maximum power dissipation of 400 mW.

What is the maximum current the diode should be allowed to handle?

Solution

$$I = P/V = 0.4/20 = 20 \text{ mA} \quad (Ans.)$$

(4) Varactor Diodes

A p-n junction is a region of high resistivity sandwiched in between two regions of relatively low resistivity. Such a junction therefore possesses capacitance, the magnitude of which is given by

$$C = \frac{\epsilon A}{W} \tag{2.1}$$

where ϵ is the permittivity of the semiconductor material, A is the area of the junction, and W is the width of the depletion layer. W

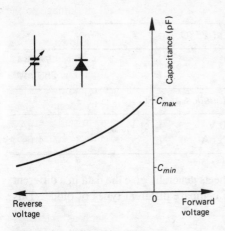

Fig. 2.14 Varactor diode characteristics

is not a constant quantity but, instead, varies with the magnitude and the polarity of the voltage applied across the junction.

Most semiconductor diodes are manufactured in such a way that their junction capacitance is minimized, but a varactor diode has been designed to have a particular range of capacitance values.

The **varactor diode** is operated with a reverse bias voltage and then its junction capacitance is inversely proportional to the square root of the bias voltage V, i.e.

$$C = \frac{K}{\sqrt{V}} \tag{2.2}$$

Fig. 2.14 shows graphically how the capacitance of a varactor diode varies with the reverse bias voltage, and it also shows the symbol for a varactor diode. Typically, the capacitance variation might be $2-12$ pF, or $20-28$ pF, or perhaps $27-72$ pF.

Example 2.6

A varactor diode has a capacitance of 5 pF when the reverse bias voltage applied across it is 4 V. Determine the diode capacitance if the bias voltage is increased to 6 V.

Solution

From equation (2.2) $5 = \dfrac{K}{\sqrt{4}}$ i.e. $K = 10$ pF $\sqrt{V}$

Therefore, when the voltage has increased to 6 V,

$C = 10/\sqrt{6} = 4.082$ pF (*Ans.*)

Data Sheets

Data sheets which can be used as an aid to the selection of the correct diode for a particular application are provided by diode manufacturers. Most diode data sheets are headed by the type number and a descriptive title. The maximum voltage and current ratings, generally at an ambient temperature of 25°C, are given. These figures should not be exceeded otherwise the diode will most probably be damaged. The main parameters that are given in a data sheet are as follows:

$I_{F(AV)}$ The maximum forward current that can flow continuously.
I_{FRM} The maximum repetitive peak forward current.
V_{RRM} The peak reverse repetitive voltage.
V_{BR} The breakdown voltage.
t_{rr} The reverse recovery time.

The 1N914 is a silicon planar switching diode. Its data sheet includes the figures given in Table 2.2.

Table 2.2

Absolute maximum ratings at 25°C

V_{RRM}	75 V	$I_{F(AV)}$	75 mA
I_{FRM}	225 mA	P	250 mW

Maximum electrical characteristics at 25°C

V_{BR} (at 100 μA)	100 V	I_R at V_{RRM}	5 μA
I_R at -20 V	25 nA	t_{rr}	4 ns

Component distributor's sheets generally give the data in a different form that makes it easier to compare different types of diode. This is shown by Table 2.3.

Table 2.3

Signal diodes

Type no.	Peak inverse voltage (V)	$I_{F(AV)}$ (mA)	Max. I_R	Application
OA200	50	80	100 nA at 50 V	General
1N914	100	75	25 nA at 20 V	Fast switch
OA90	30	10	1.1 mA at 30 V	High frequencies

Rectifier diodes

Type no.	Peak inverse voltage (V)	$I_{F(AV)}$ (A)	Max. V_F drop	Max. I_R
BY127	650	1	1.1 V at 1 A	10 μA at 650 V
1N4001	50	1	1.1 V at 1 A	10 μA at 50 V
1N4007	1000	1	1.1 V at 1 A	10 μA at 1000 V
1N5406	600	3	1.1 V at 3 A	10 μA at 600 V

Zener diodes

Type no.	Nominal voltage (V)	Tolerance	Power dissipation (mW)
1N3996	5.1	5%	10 W
BZY88	2.7,3,3.3,3.6, 4.3,4.7,5.1,6.2, 6.8,7.5,8.2,9.1, 10,11,12,13,15,16. 18,20,22,24,27,30.	5%	400 mW

3 Bipolar Transistors

Types of Bipolar Transistor

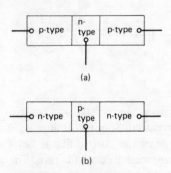

(a)

(b)

Fig. 3.1 (*a*) a p-n-p transistor, (*b*) an n-p-n transistor

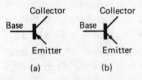

(a)   (b)

Fig. 3.2 Symbols for (*a*) a p-n-p transistor and (*b*) an n-p-n transistor

The transistor is a semiconductor device that can either amplify an electrical signal or act as an electronic switch. Basically a transistor consists of a germanium or silicon crystal which contains three separate regions. The three regions may consist of either two p-type regions separated by an n-type region (Fig. 3.1*a*) or two n-type regions separed by a p-type region (Fig. 3.1*b*). The first type of transistor is known as a p-n-p transistor and the second type as an n-p-n transistor. Both types of transistor are employed, sometimes together in the same circuit, but the discussion throughout this chapter will be in terms of the n-p-n transistor. However, for the corresponding operation of a p-n-p transistor it is merely necessary to read electron for hole, hole for electron, negative for positive, and positive for negative.

The middle of the three regions in a transistor is known as the **base** and the two outer regions are known as the **emitter** and the **collector**. In most transistors the collector region is made physically larger than the emitter region because it will be expected to dissipate a greater power. The symbol for a p-n-p transistor is given in Fig. 3.2*a* and the symbol for an n-p-n transistor in Fig. 3.2*b*. Note that the emitter lead arrowhead is pointing in different directions in the two figures, pointing inwards for the p-n-p transistor and outwards for the n-p-n transistor. It will shortly become evident that the arrowhead indicates the direction in which holes travel in the emitter.

Both p-n-p and n-p-n transistors are generally classified into one of the following groups:

(*a*) small-signal low-frequency
(*b*) low-power and medium-power low-frequency
(*c*) high-power low-frequency
(*d*) small-signal high-frequency
(*e*) medium- and high-power high-frequency
(*f*) switching.

The majority of the transistors listed in manufacturers'/distributors' catalogues are n-p-n silicon types.

The Action of a Transistor

An n-p-n transistor contains two p-n junctions and is normally operated so that one junction, the **emitter/base junction**, is forward-biased and the other, the **collector/base junction**, is reverse-biased. This is shown in Fig. 3.3 together with the directions of the various currents that flow in the transistor. The usual convention whereby the direction of current flow is opposite to the direction of electron movement has been employed.*

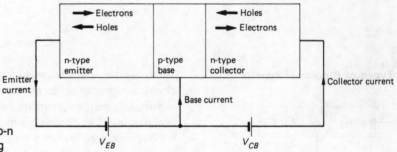

Fig. 3.3 Bias voltages for an n-p-n transistor and the currents flowing

Consider that, initially, the emitter/base bias voltage V_{EB} is zero. Then the majority charge carrier current crossing the emitter/base junction is equal to the minority charge carrier current that is flowing in the opposite direction and the net junction current is zero. The collector/base junction is reverse-biased by the bias voltage V_{CB} and so a small minority charge carrier current flows in the collector lead. This current is the reverse saturation current discussed in the previous chapter but now it is known as the **collector leakage current** and is given the symbol I_{CBO}.

If the emitter/base bias voltage is increased in the negative direction by a few tenths of a volt, the emitter/base junction is forward-biased and a majority charge carrier current flows. This current consists of electrons travelling from the emitter to the base and holes passing from the base to the emitter. Only the electron current is useful to the action of the transistor, as will soon be evident, and it is therefore made much larger than the hole current by doping the base much more lightly than the emitter. The ratio of the electron current to the total emitter current is known as the **emitter injection ratio** or the emitter efficiency, symbol γ. Typically, γ is approximately equal to 0.995 and this means that only 0.5% of the emitter current consists of holes passing from the base to the emitter.

Immediately the electrons cross the emitter/base junction, and are said to have been emitted or injected into the base, they become minority charge carriers and start to diffuse across the base towards

---

* d.c. values of current and voltage are indicated by CAPITAL suffices; a.c. values by lower-case suffices.

the collector/base junction. Because the base is fairly narrow and is also lightly doped, most of the emitted electrons reach the collector/base junction and do not recombine with a free hole on the way. On reaching the junction, the emitted electrons augment the minority charge carrier current crossing the junction and cause an increase in the collector current. The ratio of the number of electrons arriving at the collector to the number of emitted electrons is known as the **base transmission factor**, symbol β. Typically $\beta = 0.995$.

(1) The collector current is less than the emitter current because (a) part of the emitter current consists of holes that do not contribute to the collector current and (b) not all of the electrons injected into the base are successful in reaching the collector. Factor (a) is represented by the emitter injection ratio and factor (b) by the base transmission factor; hence the ratio of collector current to emitter current is equal to $\beta\gamma$. Substituting the typical values quoted for γ and β shows that, typically, the collector current is about 0.99 times the emitter current.

(2) The base current is small and has three components: (a) a current entering the base to replace the holes lost by recombination with the diffusing electrons, (b) the majority charge carrier hole current flowing from base to emitter, and (c) the collector leakage current I_{CBO}. The first two of these components are currents that flow into the base and together are greater than I_{CBO} which flows out of the base, and so the total base current flows into the base. The total current flowing into the transistor must be equal to the total current flowing out of it and hence the emitter current I_E is equal to the sum of the collector and base currents, I_C and I_B respectively, that is

$$I_E = I_C + I_B \tag{3.1}$$

Typically, I_C is equal to 0.99 I_E so that I_B is equal to 0.01 I_E.

(3) If the emitter current is varied by some means, the number of electrons arriving at the collector, and hence the collector current, will vary accordingly. The magnitude of the collector/base voltage V_{CB} has relatively little effect on the collector current as will be seen shortly. Control of the output (collector) current can thus be obtained by means of the input (emitter) current and this, in turn, can be controlled by variation of the bias voltage applied to the emitter/base junction. An increase in the forward bias voltage lowers the height of the potential barrier and allows an increased emitter current to flow; conversely, a decrease in the forward bias voltage reduces the emitter current.

(4) The ratio of the output current of a transistor to its input current in the absence of an a.c. signal is known as the **d.c. current gain** of the transistor. In the previous discussion the output current has

been the collector current I_C and the input current has been the emitter current I_E. Thus,

$$\text{d.c. current gain, } -h_{FB} = \frac{I_C}{I_E} \qquad (3.2)$$

The minus sign indicates that the input and output currents are flowing in opposite directions. By convention, a current flowing into a transistor is taken to be positive and a current flowing out is taken to be negative. Since the operation of the transistor depends upon the movement of both holes and electrons, the device is also called the **bipolar transistor**.

(5) A transistor may be connected in a circuit in one of three ways and in each case one terminal is common to both input and output. The connection is then described in terms of the common terminal; for example, the common-emitter connection has the emitter common to both input and output, the input signal is fed between the base and the emitter, and the output signal is developed between the collector and the emitter. In all connections, the base/emitter junction is always forward-biased and the collector/base junction is always reverse-biased.

The Common-base Connection

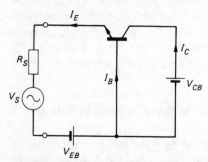

Fig. 3.4 The common-base connection

The basic arrangement of the common-base connection (or configuration) is shown in Fig. 3.4. The transistor has an alternating source of e.m.f. V_S volts r.m.s. and internal resistance R_S ohms connected to its input terminals. The alternating source is connected in series with the emitter/base voltage V_{EB} and varies the forward bias applied to the emitter/base junction.

During negative half-cycles of the source e.m.f., the forward bias applied to the junction is increased, the potential barrier is lowered, and an enhanced emitter current flows into the transistor. Conversely, during positive half-cycles the emitter current is decreased and in this way the collector current is caused to vary in accordance with the waveform of the applied signal voltage. The collector/base bias battery V_{CB} has negligible internal resistance and so the collector/base voltage remains constant as the collector current varies. The collector circuit is said to be *short-circuited* so far as alternating currents are concerned.

In a common-base amplifier circuit an important parameter is the **short-circuit current gain** of the transistor, symbol h_{fb}. The short-circuit current gain is defined as the ratio of a *change* in collector current to the *change* in emitter current producing it, with the collector/base voltage maintained constant, that is

$$h_{fb} = \frac{\delta I_C}{\delta I_E} = \frac{I_c}{I_e} \text{ when } V_{CB} \text{ is constant} \qquad (3.3)$$

The *short-circuit* current gain is specified since analysis shows that the current gain is a function of the value of any resistance placed in the collector circuit. For the common-base circuit, however, the difference between the short-circuit current gain and the current gain for any particular collector load resitance is very small for all resistance values used in practical circuits and is usually neglected.

Example 3.1

In a certain transistor a change in emitter current of 1 mA produces a change in collector current of 0.99 mA. Determine the short-circuit current gain of the transistor.

Solution

$$\text{Current gain } h_{fb} = \frac{\delta I_C}{\delta I_E} = \frac{I_c}{I_e} = \frac{0.99}{1} = 0.99 \quad (Ans.)$$

This is a typical value for the short-circuit current gain of a transistor connected in the common-base configuration. It should be evident that h_{fb} must be less than unity, because the emitter current is the sum of the base and collector currents. Clearly, then, a common-base transistor must have a current gain of less than unity but, if a resistor is connected in the collector circuit, as shown in Fig. 3.5, both voltage and power gains are possible.

The output voltage is developed across the collector load resistor and, since the internal resistance of the collector supply is negligible, the top end of the resistor is effectively at earth potential so far as alternating currents are concerned. Thus the output signal voltage is taken from between the collector terminal and earth.

The source of the output power is the collector/base bias battery, the transistor effectively acting as a device for the conversion of d.c. power from the battery into the a.c. power supplied to the load.

In the common-base amplifier the input signal voltage and the output signal voltage are in phase with each other, as shown by the waveforms of Fig. 3.5. Consider the input signal voltage to be passing through zero and increasing in the negative direction. The forward bias of the base/emitter junction is then increased and this results in an increase in the emitter current. The collector current is increased and the voltage drop across the collector load resistor R_L

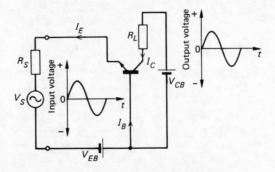

Fig. 3.5 The basic common-base amplifier

increases also and this makes the collector/base potential less positive. Thus a negative increment in the input signal voltage produces a negative increment in the output signal voltage.

The common-base connected transistor is rarely, if ever, used at audio frequencies because of its low current gain and its inconvenient values of input and output impedance.

The Common-emitter Connection

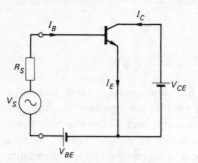

Fig. 3.6 The common-emitter connection

In practice, transistors are most often used in the common-emitter configuration shown in Fig. 3.6.

The emitter/base junction is forward-biased by the battery V_{BE} and the collector/base junction is reverse-biased by a potential equal to $(V_{CE} - V_{BE})$. However, since the voltage of the collector/emitter bias battery V_{CE} is much larger than the emitter/base bias voltage V_{BE}, the reverse bias voltage may often be taken as merely equal to V_{CE} volts.

When a transistor is connected in this way, the input current is the base current and not the emitter current as previously. The operation of the transistor is unchanged from that previously described and the d.c. current gain h_{FE} is the ratio

$$h_{FE} = \frac{I_C}{I_B} \tag{3.4}$$

During the positive half-cycles of the input signal voltage V_S, the forward bias of the emitter/base junction is increased, and so the emitter current I_E is increased by an amount δI_E. The collector current is also increased, by an amount $\delta I_C = h_{fb}\delta I_E$, and so is the base (input) current, by an amount

$$\delta I_B = \delta I_E - \delta I_C = \delta I_E(1 - h_{fb})$$

Conversely, during negative half-cycles of the input signal voltage the three currents are reduced in magnitude.

The **short-circuit current gain** of a common-emitter connected transistor, symbol h_{fe}, is defined as the ratio of a *change* in collector current δI_C to the *change* in base current δI_B producing it, the collector/emitter voltage being maintained constant, that is

$$h_{fe} = \frac{\delta I_C}{\delta I_B} = \frac{I_c}{I_b} \text{ when } V_{CE} \text{ is constant} \tag{3.5}$$

$$h_{fe} = \frac{h_{fb}I_e}{I_e - h_{fb}I_e}$$

$$= \frac{h_{fb}I_e}{I_e(1 - h_{fb})}$$

$$= \frac{h_{fb}}{1 - h_{fb}} \tag{3.6}$$

Typical values for the short-circuit current gain h_{fb} of a common-base transistor are in the neighbourhood of unity and thus the common-emitter connection can give a considerable current gain.

The a.c. and the d.c. current gains of a transistor are not usually of the same value, their difference being dependent upon the d.c. collector current flowing. Usually, little error is introduced by assuming that h_{FE} is equal to h_{fe}. In any case, the value of h_{FE} (or h_{fe}) can vary considerably between two transistors of the same type and hence of the same nominal current gain.

Example 3.2

A transistor exhibits a change of 0.995 mA in its collector current for a change of 1 mA in its emitter current. Calculate (a) its common-base short-circuit current gain and (b) its common-emitter short-circuit current gain.

Solution
(a) Common-base short-circuit current gain

$$h_{fb} = \frac{I_c}{I_e} = \frac{0.995}{1} = 0.995 \quad (Ans.)$$

(b) Common-emitter short-circuit current gain

$$h_{fe} = \frac{I_c}{I_b} = \frac{h_{fb}}{1 - h_{fb}} = \frac{0.995}{1 - 0.995} = 199 \quad (Ans.)$$

When a load resistor R_L is connected in the collector circuit (Fig. 3.7) the current gain of the transistor is no longer equal to the short-circuit value but is somewhat less. The actual value of the current gain is dependent upon the value of the collector load resistor R_L, decreasing with increase in R_L.

To obtain expressions for the voltage gain and the power gain of a transistor connected with common emitter: let the r.m.s. voltage and internal resistance of the voltage source applied to the input terminals of the transistor be V_S volts and R_S ohms respectively, and let the input resistance of the transistor be R_{IN} ohms.

Then (Fig. 3.8), the a.c. input current to the transistor, I_b, is

$$I_b = \frac{V_S}{R_S + R_{IN}}$$

and the voltage V_{IN} appearing across the transistor input terminals is

$$V_{IN} = I_b R_{IN} \quad \text{or} \quad I_b = \frac{V_{IN}}{R_{IN}}$$

The output or collector current I_c is

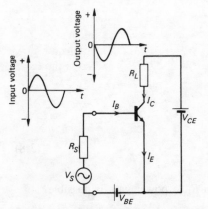

Fig. 3.7 The basic common-emitter amplifier

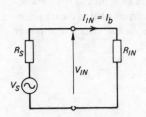

Fig. 3.8 Circuit for the calculation of the input current to a transistor

$$I_c = \frac{h_{fe}V_{IN}}{R_{IN}}$$

This current flows through the collector load resistance R_L and develops the output voltage V_{OUT} across it, therefore

$$V_{OUT} = \frac{h_{fe}V_{IN}}{R_{IN}} R_L$$

and the **voltage gain** A_v is

$$A_v = \frac{V_{OUT}}{V_{IN}} = \frac{h_{fe}R_L}{R_{IN}} \tag{3.7}$$

Since the short-circuit current gain h_{fe} is greater than unity and the collector load resistance R_L is usually greater than the input resistance R_{IN} of the transistor, a voltage gain is readily achieved.

Now consider the power gain of a common-emitter transistor. This is the ratio of the power delivered to the load to the power delivered to the transistor.

The input power P_{IN} to the transistor is (see Fig. 3.8)

$$P_{IN} = I_b^2 R_{IN}$$

and the output power P_{OUT} is

$$P_{OUT} = (h_{fe}I_b)^2 R_L$$

Therefore the **power gain** A_p is

$$A_p = \frac{P_{OUT}}{P_{IN}} = \frac{h_{fe}^2 I_b^2 R_L}{I_b^2 R_{IN}}$$

$$A_p = \frac{h_{fe}^2 R_L}{R_{IN}} = A_v A_i \tag{3.8}$$

Again, since R_L is greater than R_{IN} a power gain is possible.

Example 3.3

A transistor is connected with common-emitter in a circuit and has a collector load resistance of 2000 Ω. The short-circuit current gain of the transistor is 100 and its input resistance is 1000 Ω. Calculate the voltage and power gains of the transistor.

Solution
From equation (3.7),

$$\text{Voltage gain} = \frac{h_{fe}R_L}{R_{IN}} = \frac{100 \times 2000}{1000} = 200 \quad (Ans.)$$

From equation (3.8),

$$\text{Power gain} = \frac{h_{fe}^2 R_L}{R_{IN}} = 200 \times 100 = 20\,000 \quad (Ans.)$$

The Common-collector Connection

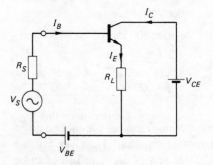

Fig. 3.9 The basic common-collector amplifier

The third way in which a transistor may be connected is shown in Fig. 3.9. The collector terminal is now common to both input and output circuits and the load resistor is connected in the emitter circuit. With this configuration the base current is the input current and the emitter current is the output current. The **short-circuit current gain** is defined as

Short-circuit current gain

$$h_{fc} = \frac{\delta I_E}{\delta I_B} = \frac{I_e}{I_b} \text{ when } V_{CE} \text{ is constant} \tag{3.9}$$

$$= \frac{I_e}{I_e - I_c}$$

$$= \frac{I_e}{I_e(1 - h_{fb})}$$

$$= \frac{1}{1 - h_{fb}} \tag{3.10}$$

$$= h_{fe} + 1 \tag{3.11}$$

The short-circuit current gain of a transistor connected in the common-collector configuration is approximately equal to the short-circuit gain of the same transistor connected with common-emitter. The current gain when a load is connected in the emitter circuit is not equal to the short-circuit current gain but is reduced by an amount that is dependent on the value of the emitter load.

Expressions (3.7) and (3.8) may be used to determine the voltage and power gains of a common-collector circuit. Now, however, the input resistance is considerably larger than the load resistance and a voltage gain of less than unity is obtained.

The main use of the common-collector circuit − or the *emitter-follower* as it is usually called − is as a buffer which is connected between a high impedance source and a low impedance load.

A comparison between the main characteristics of the three transistor configurations is given in Table 3.1 (see p. 36).

Transistor Static Characteristics

A number of current/voltage plots are available in the study of the operation of a transistor in a circuit. The resulting curves, which are known as the static characteristic curves, give information on the

Table 3.1

Characteristic	Common-base	Common-emitter	Common-collector
Short-circuit current gain	h_{fb}	$h_{fc} = \dfrac{h_{fb}}{1 - h_{fb}}$	$h_{fc} = \dfrac{1}{1 - h_{fb}}$
Voltage gain	Good	Better than common-base	Unity or less
Input resistance	Low 30 to 100 Ω	Medium 800 to 5000 Ω	High 5000 to 500 000 Ω
Output resistance	High 10^5 to 10^6 Ω	Medium 10 000 to 50 000 Ω	Low 50 to 1000 Ω

value of current flowing into or out of one terminal for either a given current flowing into or out of another terminal or a given voltage applied between two terminals. Four sets of characteristics can be plotted for each configuration: (*a*) the input characteristic, (*b*) the transfer characteristic, (*c*) the output characteristic, and (*d*) the mutual characteristic. In this book, however, the characteristics for the common-base and the common-collector circuits will not be discussed. Two versions of set (*c*) are available.

The method of determining the static characteristics of a transistor is to connect the transistor into a suitable circuit and then to vary the appropriate currents and/or voltages in a number of discrete steps, noting the corresponding values of other currents at each step. Fig. 3.10 shows a suitable circuit for the determination of the characteristics of an n-p-n transistor in the common-emitter configuration.

The collector and base currents are shown as flowing into the transistor and are therefore, by definition, positive; the emitter current is shown flowing out of the transistor and must be taken as negative. If the characteristics of a p-n-p transistor had to be measured, the polarities of the two batteries would need to be reversed.

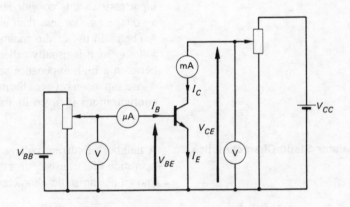

Fig. 3.10 Circuit for the determination of the static characteristics of a common-emitter connected transistor

(a) Common-emitter Input Characteristic

The **input characteristic** shows the way in which the base current varies with change in the base/emitter voltage, the collector/emitter voltage remaining constant. The method of determining the input characteristic is to maintain the collector/emitter voltage constant at a convenient value and increase the base/emitter voltage in a number of discrete steps, noting the base current at each step. The procedure is then repeated for a different but constant value of collector/emitter voltage V_{CE}, since change in this voltage has an effect on the input characteristic. A typical input characteristic is shown in Fig. 3.11.

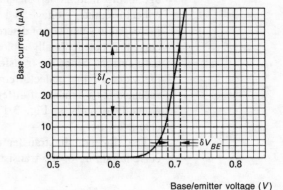

Fig. 3.11 Common-emitter input characteristic
$\delta V_{BE} = 0.71 - 0.69 = 0.02$ V
$\delta I_B = 36 - 14 = 22$ μA

The input resistance, h_{ie}, for a given base/emitter voltage V_{BE} is given by the reciprocal of the slope of the curve at that point. For example, consider the short-circuit input resistance of the transistor at the point $V_{BE} = 0.7$ V.

$$h_{ie} = \frac{\delta V_{BE}}{\delta I_B} = \frac{V_{be}}{I_b} \quad (V_{CE} \text{constant}) \tag{3.12}$$

$$= \frac{0.02}{22 \times 10^{-6}} = 909 \ \Omega$$

The corresponding p-n-p characteristics would have negative values of I_B, V_{BE} and V_{CE}.

Since the input chracteristic is non-linear, the a.c. input resistance of a transistor will vary with the base current. Thus

when $I_B = 2$ μA $\quad h_{ie} = 6.7$ kΩ.

The d.c. input resistance h_{IE} is the ratio V_{BE}/I_B. At the point of measurement

$$h_{IE} = 0.7/25 \times 10^{-6} = 28 \text{ k}\Omega.$$

It is evident that considerable difference exists between the values of h_{IE} and h_{ie}. If the point of measurement is reduced below about $V_{BE} = 0.68$ V, the slope of the input characteristic is smaller and the a.c. input resistance h_{ie} will be larger so that the difference between h_{IE} and h_{ie} will be much less. For base currents of the order of a few tens of microamps, h_{ie} is typically about 3 kΩ.

(b) Common-emitter Current-transfer Characteristic

The **transfer characteristic** shows how the collector current changes with changes in the base current, the collector/emitter voltage being held at a constant value. For this measurement the collector/emitter voltage is kept constant and the base current is increased in a number of discrete steps and at each step the collector current is noted. Finally a plot is made of collector current against base current. Since the transfer characteristic is not independent of the value of the collector/emitter voltage, the procedure can be repeated for a number of different collector/emitter voltages to give a family of curves, Fig. 3.12 showing a typical n-p-n transistor characteristic.

The slope of the transfer characteristic gives the short-circuit current gain h_{fe} of the transistor.

$$h_{fe} = \frac{\delta I_C}{\delta I_B} = \frac{I_c}{I_b} = \frac{1 \times 10^{-3}}{4 \times 10^{-6}} = 250$$

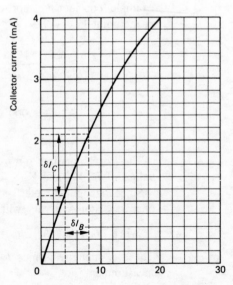

Fig. 3.12 Common-emitter current-transfer characteristic
$\delta I_C = 2.1 - 1.1 = 1$ mA
$\delta I_B = 8 - 4 = 4$ μA

(c) Common-emitter Output Characteristic

The **output characteristic** illustrates the changes that occur in collector current with changes in collector/emitter voltage, for constant value of base current. Alternatively, the collector current can be plotted against collector/emitter voltage for constant values of base/emitter voltage. The base current, or the base/emitter voltage, is set to a convenient value and is then maintained constant and the collector/emitter voltage is increased from zero in a number of discrete steps, the collector current being noted at each step. The collector/emitter voltage is then restored to zero and the base current, or the base/emitter voltage, is increased to another convenient value and the procedure repeated. In this way a family of curves (see Figs. 3.13 and 3.14) can be obtained. For the corresponding p-n-p characteristic the polarities of I_C, I_B and V_{CE} should be changed to negative. The slope $\delta I_C/\delta V_{BE}$ of the output characteristic is the output admittance, h_{oe}, of the transistor.

The output resistance of the transistor is equal to the *reciprocal* of the slope of the output characteristic. From Fig. 3.13 the output resistance at the point $V_{CE}=6$ V and $I_B=30$ μA is

$$R_{OUT} = \frac{1}{h_{oe}} = \frac{\delta V_{CE}}{\delta I_C} = \frac{V_{ce}}{I_c} \quad (I_B \text{ constant}) \qquad (3.13)$$

$$= \frac{2}{0.2 \times 10^{-3}} = 10\ 000\ \Omega$$

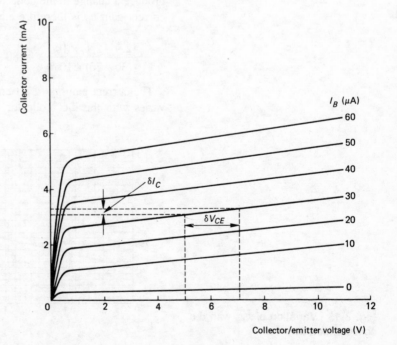

Fig. 3.13 Common-emitter output characteristics
$\delta V_{CE}=7-5=2$ V
$\delta I_C=3.3-3.1=0.2$ mA

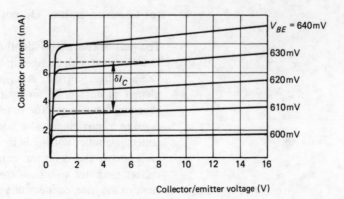

Fig. 3.14 Common-emitter output characteristics with V_{BE} as input

When a characteristic is non-linear its slope will vary according to the point of measurement and therefore the point of measurement should always be quoted. It is usual, unless specified otherwise, to measure the slope in the middle of the characteristic. For the greatest accuracy the increments taken either side of the chosen point should be as small as possible although this has not been done in this chapter in order to clarify the diagrams.

The output characteristics of Fig. 3.13 can also be used to determine the short-circuit current gain h_{fe} of the transistor, since, for a given value of collector/emitter voltage V_{CE}, the change in collector current δI_C produced by a change in base current δI_B can be obtained by projecting from the appropriate curves. Thus, for $V_{CE} = 4$ V a change in the base current from 20 μA to 30 μA will produce a change in the collector current from 2.1 to 2.9 mA. The current gain h_{fe} is therefore equal to

$$\frac{(2.9 - 2.1) \times 10^{-3}}{(30 - 20) \times 10^{-6}} = 80$$

The current gain h_{fe} of a transistor is not a constant quantity but varies with the d.c. collector current. Fig. 3.15 shows a typical

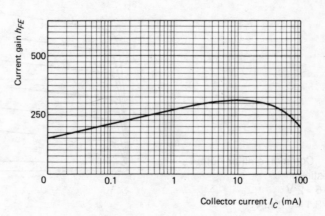

Fig. 3.15 Variation of h_{FE} with d.c collector current

graph of h_{FE} plotted against I_C. Manufacturer's data generally quote the collector current at which the maximum value of h_{fe} is obtained, e.g. for the BC 108 the typical h_{fe} is 180 at $I_C = 2\ mA$. (Both h_{fe} and h_{FE} vary.)

It will be seen that Fig. 3.13 shows a collector current flowing even when the base current is zero. This current is the *common-emitter leakage current*, symbol I_{CEO}, which is related to the common-base leakage current I_{CBO} according to the expression

$$I_{CEO} = I_{CBO}(1 + h_{FE}) \qquad (3.14)$$

The collector leakage current I_{CBO} of a common-base transistor is extremely temperature-sensitive and is approximately doubled for every 12°C rise in temperature for silicon transistors and every 8°C rise for germanium transistors. However, the leakage current of a silicon transistor at a given temperature is much less than the leakage current of an equivalent germanium transistor at the same temperature.

Typically, I_{CBO} at 20°C for a germanium transistor may be about 10 μA but only about 10 nA for a silicon transistor.

(d) Common-emitter Mutual Characteristic

The **mutual characteristics** of a common-emitter connected transistor show the changes in collector current that occur with changes in the base/emitter voltage, with the collector/emitter voltage held constant. Fig. 3.16 shows a typical mutual characteristic. The slope of the mutual characteristic is the mutual conductance g_m of the transistor.

Thus, when V_{BE} changes from 0.6 V to 0.65 V the resulting change in I_C is from 1.5 mA to 11.5 mA and so

$$g_m = \delta I_C / \delta V_{BE} = 10 \times 10^{-3} / 0.05 = 200\ \text{mS}$$

The mutual conductance can also be determined from the output characteristics of Fig. 3.14 using a similar method to that employed to obtain h_{fe} from Fig. 3.13. When $V_{CE} = 8$ V, a change in V_{BE} from 610 mV to 630 mV causes I_C to vary from 3.3 mA to 6.7 mA. Hence

$$g_m = \delta I_C / \delta V_{BE} = \frac{3.4 \times 10^{-3}}{20 \times 10^{-3}} = 170\ \text{mS}$$

Also $\quad g_m = \dfrac{\delta I_C}{\delta V_{BE}} \qquad (3.15)$

$$= \frac{\delta I_C}{\delta I_B} \times \frac{\delta I_B}{\delta V_{BE}}$$

$$= \frac{h_{fe}}{h_{ie}} \qquad (3.16)$$

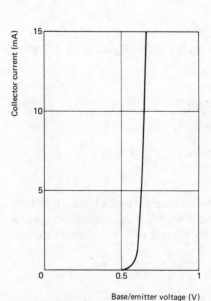

Fig. 3.16 Common-emitter mutual characteristic

The mutual conductance g_m depends only on the d.c. collector current I_c, according to the equation

$$g_m = \frac{I_c}{26} \text{ mS} \tag{3.17}$$

where I_c is in mA.

From equation (3.7), the voltage gain of a transistor is given by $A_v = A_i R_L / R_{IN}$. This can be written as $A_v = h_{fe} R_L / h_{ie}$ and using equation (3.16)

$$A_v = g_m R_L \tag{3.18}$$

Thermal and Frequency Effects

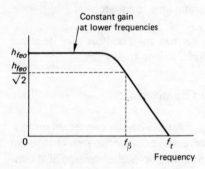

Fig. 3.17 Variation of $|h_{fe}|$ with frequency

Frequency Characteristics

The current gain of a transistor is not the same value at all frequencies, but, instead, falls off at the higher frequencies (see Fig. 3.17). The frequency at which the magnitude of the current gain h_{fe} has fallen to $1/\sqrt{2}$ times its low-frequency value h_{feo} is known as the **cut-off frequency** f_β of the transistor. Eventually, at some frequency f_t, $|h_{fe}|$ falls to unity. The high-frequency performance of a transistor is often quoted by the manufacturer in terms of a parameter f_t, where

$$f_t = |h_{fe}| \cdot f \tag{3.19}$$

f being any frequency.

f_t is known as the **transition frequency** or as the *common-emitter gain-bandwidth product*.

Example 3.4

A transistor has $f_t = 500$ MHz. What is its current gain at (a) 100 MHz, (b) 10 MHz?

Solution

(a) $f_t = 500 \text{ MHz} = |h_{fe}| \times 100 \text{ MHz}$

$|h_{fe}| = 5$ (*Ans.*)

(b) $f_t = 500 \text{ MHz} = |h_{fe}| \times 10 \text{ MHz}$

$|h_{fe}| = 50$ (*Ans.*)

Fig. 3.18 shows how the transition frequency of a typical transistor varies with the collector current. Clearly, if the device is to operate at a high frequency, the collector current must be carefully chosen.

Thermal Runaway

An increase in the temperature of the collector/base junction will cause the collector leakage current I_{CBO} to increase. The increase in

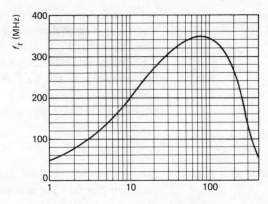

Fig. 3.18 Variation of f_t with collector current

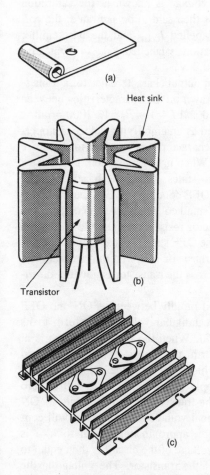

Fig. 3.19 Three kinds of heat sink

collector current produces an increase in the power dissipated at the junction and this, in turn, further increases the temperature of the junction and so gives further increase in I_{CBO}. The process is cumulative and, particularly in the common-emitter connection of a germanium transistor, could lead to the eventual destruction of the transistor. In practice, thermal runaway is prevented in well-designed circuits by the use of stabilization circuitry that compensates for any increase in I_{CBO} and also, for power transistors, by the use of a heat sink to provide rapid conduction of heat away from the junction. Thermal runaway is rarely a problem with silicon transistors.

The manufacturer of a transistor quotes the maximum permissible power that can be dissipated within the transistor without damage. The power dissipated within a transistor is predominantly the power which is dissipated at its collector-base junction, and this, in turn, is equal to the d.c. power taken from the collector supply voltage minus the total output power (d.c. power plus a.c. power). For transistors handling small signals, the power dissipated at the collector is small and there is generally little problem. When the power dissipated by the transistor is large enough to cause the junction temperature to rise to a dangerous level, it is necessary to improve the rate at which heat is removed from the device. Power transistors are constructed with their collector terminal connected to their metallic case. To increase the area from which the heat is removed the case of the transistor can be bolted on to a sheet of metal known as a **heat sink**. Heat will move from the transistor to the heat sink by conduction and be removed from the sink by convection and radiation.

The simplest heat sink is shown in Fig. 3.19*a*. It consists of a push-fit clip that can be screwed on to a metal chassis, the transistor being a push-fit into the hole. The greater the power dissipated within a transistor, the larger the surface area of the heat sink required to remove sufficient heat to keep the junction temperature within safe limits. To prevent the heat sink occupying too much space within an equipment, it is common to employ structures of the kinds shown in Figs. 3.19b and 3.19c.

For maximum efficiency a heat sink should (i) be in excellent thermal contact with the transistor case, (ii) have the largest possible surface area and be painted matt black, and (iii) be mounted in a position such that a free flow of air past it is possible.

The Bipolar Transistor as a Switch

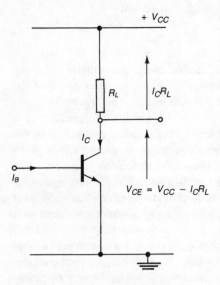

Fig. 3.20 Voltages in a simple bipolar transistor circuit

When a transistor is used as a switch it is either biased to be non-conducting or OFF, or it is biased to conduct the maximum possible current, or be ON. If the base current of a transistor with a collector resistor R_L is gradually increased from zero the collector current will increase as well, since $I_C = h_{FE}I_B$. The collector-emitter voltage V_{CE} will fall since, from Fig. 3.20, $V_{CE} = V_{CC} - I_C R_L$. Eventually, the point will be reached at which V_{CE} has fallen to its minimum possible value. This minimum voltage is known as the saturation voltage $V_{CE(SAT)}$. The transistor is then said to be saturated; the collector current at saturation is labelled $I_{C(SAT)}$ and the base-emitter voltage that *just* produces saturation is labelled $V_{BE(SAT)}$. Typically, $V_{BE(SAT)}$ is 0.7 V and $V_{CE(SAT)}$ is 0.2 V.

Fig. 3.21 shows a typical set of output characteristics for a transistor. A d.c. load line has been drawn on the characteristics between the points $V_{CE} = V_{CC} = 12$ V, $I_C = 0$ and $I_C = V_{CC}/R_L = 12/2000 = 6$ mA, $V_{CE} = 0$. When a transistor is used as an amplifying device, its operation is restricted to part of its characteristics in order to minimize distortion of the applied signal. When used as a switch, a transistor is rapidly switched between two states. When the base current is zero the transistor is held in its OFF condition. When the transistor is OFF it only conducts the very small collector leakage current. The voltage dropped across the collector resistor is negligible and so the voltage across the transistor in the OFF state is equal to the collector supply voltage V_{CC}. When the transistor is driven into saturation it is in its ON state. The voltage across the transistor is now its *saturation voltage* $V_{CE(SAT)}$.

The transistor can be switched rapidly between its ON and OFF states by the application of a rectangular voltage waveform to its base-emitter terminal (Fig. 3.22). When the input waveform is at zero potential with respect to earth, the transistor will be switched into its OFF state; the voltage which appears at the output terminals is then equal to the collector supply voltage since there will be zero voltage drop across R_L. When the transistor is switched into its ON state by the rectangular base signal voltage, the transistor will conduct heavily and a large voltage, approximately equal to V_{CC}, is dropped across R_L. The output voltage of the circuit is then equal to the saturation voltage $V_{CE(SAT)}$ of the transistor. The voltage at the output terminals of the circuit switches between $V_{CE(SAT)}$ and V_{CC}

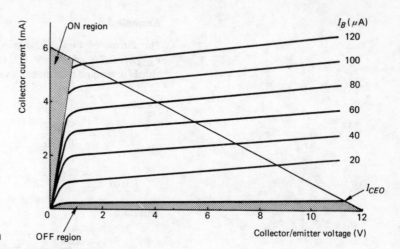

Fig. 3.21 The transistor as a switch

volts. It should be noted that when the input signal voltage is positive the output voltage is $V_{CE(SAT)}$, and when the input signal voltage is zero the output voltage is V_{CC} volts (See Fig. 3.23). This means that the input waveform has been inverted; and the circuit has performed the logical function NOT. A typical value for the base-emitter voltage V_{BE} when a transistor is ON is in the range 0.6 V to 1.0 V depending on the type and the rating of the device.

The more positive (less negative) voltage level can be regarded as representing logical 1 and the less positive level as giving logical 0. This convention is known as **positive logic**. Conversely, logical 1 can be taken as being the least positive, or more negative, voltage level with the more positive voltage being labelled as logical 0. This second convention is known as **negative logic**. Clearly, the convention employed in a particular case must be clearly stated, or understood. Positive logic is the more commonly employed.

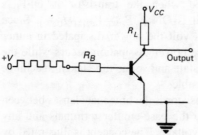

Fig. 3.22 Switching a transistor

Example 3.5

The transistor used in the circuit of Fig. 3.22 has $V_{CE(SAT)}=0.15$ V, $R_L=1200\ \Omega$ and $V_{CC}=5$ V. Calculate (a) the saturated collector current $I_{C(SAT)}$ and (b) the power dissipated in R_L when the transistor is (i) ON and (ii) OFF.

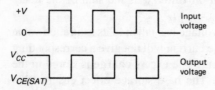

Fig. 3.23 Input and output waveforms of the transistor switch

Solution

(a) $I_{C(SAT)} = \dfrac{(5-0.15)}{1200} = 4.042$ mA (*Ans.*)

(b) (i) $P = (4.042 \times 10^{-3})^2 \times 1200 = 19.6$ mW (*Ans.*)

(ii) $I_C = 0$ so $P=0$ (*Ans.*)

Example 3.6

The circuit of Fig. 3.22 has $V_{CC}=12$ V, $R_L=1$ kΩ, $V_{CE(SAT)}=0.2$ V, $V_{BE(SAT)}=0.7$ V and $R_B=30$ kΩ. If a 5 V voltage is applied to the input terminals determine the minimum value of h_{FE} which will produce saturation.

Solution

$$I_B = \frac{5-0.7}{30 \times 10^3} = 143 \ \mu A$$

$$I_{C(SAT)} = \frac{12-0.2}{1000} = 11.8 \ mA$$

Therefore

$$h_{FE(MIN)} = \frac{11.8 \times 10^{-3}}{143 \times 10^{-6}} = 82.5 \quad (Ans.)$$

Speed of Switching

Rapid switching between the ON and the OFF states of a transistor is desirable in order to minimize the power dissipation within the device. The power dissipated when the transistor is OFF is $P_{OFF}=V_{CC}I_{CEO}\simeq0$, and when it is ON is $P_{ON}=V_{CE(SAT)}I_{C(SAT)}$. Since $V_{CE(SAT)}$ is only a fraction of a volt the power dissipated in either state is very small. Most of the power dissipation occurs while the transistor is actually changing state and so the time taken to achieve this should be as small as possible.

The switching speed of a transistor is the time that elapses between the application of a voltage to the base-emitter terminals and any resulting change in the output voltage. The concept is illustrated by Fig. 3.24. The base-emitter voltage pulse, Fig. 3.24*a*, does not cause the collector-emitter voltage, Fig. 3.24*b*, to change its state instantaneously. Instead, it remains at the supply voltage V_{CC} volts for a short time and has only fallen to 0.9 V_{CC} after a time period t_d. This is the time needed to fully charge the capacitance of the base-emitter p-n junction. After t_d seconds the collector-emitter voltage V_{CE} falls at a rate that is limited by the need to charge the collector-base capacitance, but eventually it reaches its saturation value $V_{CE(SAT)}$. The **fall-time** t_f is the time taken for V_{CE} to fall from 0.9 V_{CC} to 0.1 V_{CC}. The **turn-on time** t_{ON} is the sum of the delay time and the fall-time, i.e. $t_{ON}=t_d+t_f$.

Once the collector-emitter voltage has fallen to its saturation value any further increase in the base current will not give a corresponding increase in the collector current. The **excess charge** is stored in the base region of the transistor. The base storage effect ensures that when the base-emitter voltage is reduced to zero the transistor does not instantaneously cease conduction. There is an initial **storage**

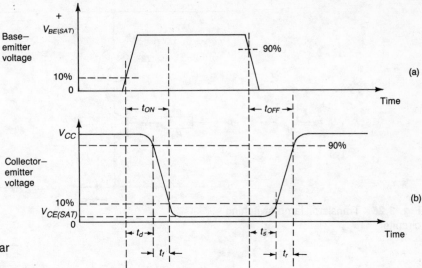

Fig. 3.24 Switching a bipolar transistor

delay t_s during which the excess base charge is removed from the transistor. At the end of this period the collector current falls, and so the collector-emitter voltage rises towards V_{CC} volts. The rate at which the collector-emitter voltage is able to increase is limited by the need for the junction and load capacitances to be discharged. The **risetime** t_r is the time taken for the collector-emitter voltage to increase from $0.1\ V_{CC}$ to $0.9\ V_{CC}$ volts.

The **turn-off time** t_{OFF} is equal to the sum of the storage time and the risetime, i.e. $t_{OFF} = t_s + t_r$.

Typical figures for the turn-on and the turn-off times of a transistor are $t_{OFF} = 360$ ns and $t_{ON} = 55$ ns for a general-purpose transistor and $t_{OFF} = 125$ ns and $t_{ON} = 27$ ns for a switching transistor.

Switching Circuits

A simple switching circuit can be designed using a single transistor with the load in the collector circuit and a current-limiting resistor in the base circuit. A basic lamp-control circuit is shown in both Figs 3.25*a* and *b*.

When the base current is zero there will be zero collector current and the lamp will not light. When a voltage pulse is applied, Fig. 3.25*a*, or the switch is closed, Fig. 3.25*b*, a base current, and hence a collector current, flows and the lamp lights. The transistor that is employed should have adequate current gain, a low collector saturation voltage, and, if high-speed operation is desired, low values of turn-on and turn-off times. The value of the base resistor

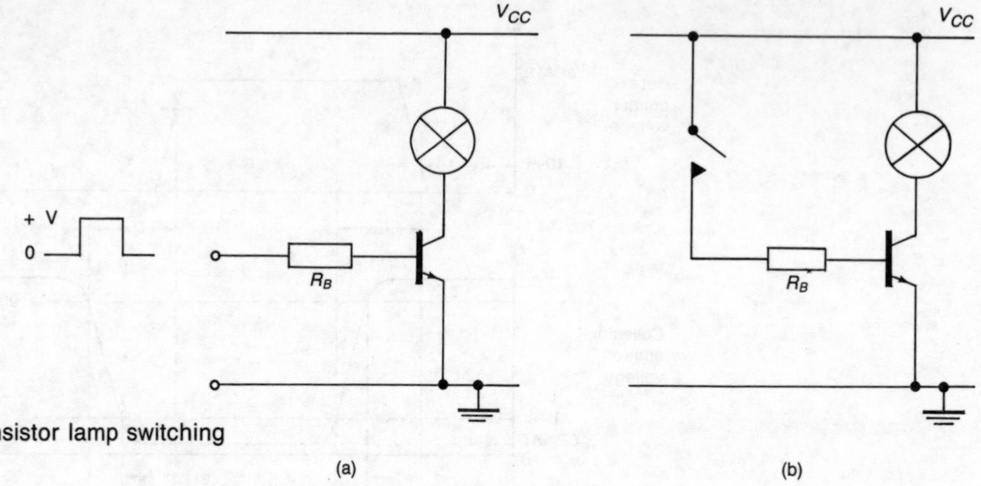

V_{CC} V_{CC}

(a)   (b)

Fig. 3.25 Transistor lamp switching circuits

R_B should be chosen to ensure that the transistor saturates. The base current required will need to be somewhat greater than $I_{C(SAT)}/h_{FE}$ because the value of h_{FE} will fall as the collector-emitter voltage approaches its saturation value. The minimum value of h_{FE} obtained from the data sheet should be used.

Applying Kirchoff's law to the base circuit of Fig. 3.25a gives

$$V = I_B R_B + V_{BE},$$

or

$$R_B = \frac{V - V_{BE}}{I_B} \tag{3.20}$$

If I_B is to be the value which just produces the saturation collector current $I_{C(SAT)}$ then V_{BE} should be the saturation value $V_{BE(SAT)}$ obtained from the data sheet.

Example 3.7

In the circuit given in Fig. 3.25a the collector supply voltage V_{CC} is 5 V and the resistance of the lamp when lit is 50 Ω. The transistor parameters are $h_{FE} = 100$, $V_{BE(SAT)} = 0.7$ V and $V_{CE(SAT)} = 0.2$ V. Calculate the necessary value of the base resistor if the applied voltage is 5 V.

Solution

The saturated collector current is

$$I_{C(SAT)} = \frac{5 - 0.2}{50} = 96 \text{ mA.}$$

The minimum base current for saturation is

$$I_{C(SAT)}/h_{FE} = \frac{96 \times 10^{-3}}{100} = 960 \ \mu\text{A.}$$

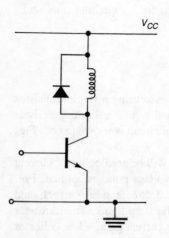

Fig. 3.26 Transistor switching an inductive load

From equation (3.20),

$$R_B = \frac{5-0.7}{960 \times 10^{-6}} = 4479 \ \Omega$$

A lower value should be selected to ensure the transistor saturates. The nearest preferred value is 4300 Ω. (*Ans.*)

When the collector load is inductive, perhaps a relay coil for example, a diode should be connected as shown in Fig. 3.26. Otherwise, a large collector-emitter voltage may be generated when the transistor turns OFF, and this might damage the device.

The Construction of Transistors

A number of different methods of manufacturing transistors have been developed since the invention of the transistor in 1948 and a description of many of them is outside the scope of this book. The most commonly employed type of transistor is the silicon planar transistor and only the construction of this type will be presented.

The construction of a **silicon planar transistor** is shown in Fig. 3.27. The steps involved in the manufacture of a silicon planar transistor are as follows: a wafer of n-type silicon is oxidized to a depth of approximately 1 micron (Fig. 3.28*a*) and then the oxide is partially etched off (Fig. 3.28*b*). Next the wafer is exposed to a vapour of the acceptor element boron and the impurity is allowed to diffuse into the wafer to a predetermined depth. At the same time the wafer surface is reoxidized (Fig. 3.28*c*). A part of the reoxidized surface is then etched away (Fig. 3.28*d*) and the wafer is exposed to a vapour of the donor element phosphorus; it is also reoxidized again (Fig. 3.28*e*). The wafer now contains a layer of p-type material that will form the base of the transistor and a layer of n-type material that provides the emitter. The wafer is then etched to separate the base and emitter regions on the surface of the wafer (Fig. 3.28*f*) and finally (Fig. 3.28*g*) metal contacts are alloyed on to the etched areas.

The wafer is cut to the required size, mounted on a suitable collector contact, and then leads are connected to the base and emitter contacts.

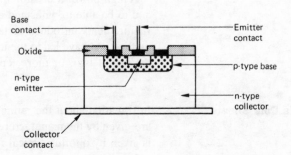

Fig. 3.27 Construction of a silicon planar transistor

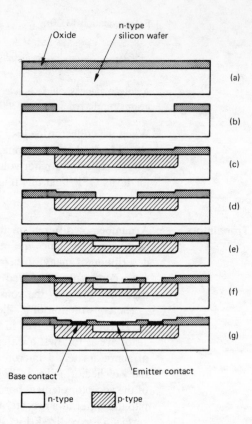

Fig. 3.28 The stages in the manufacture of a silicon planar transistor

The construction of a planar transistor requires a relatively thick collector wafer in order to give adequate mechanical support to the other layers and this increases the resistance of the collector. For some applications the collector resistance is too large and must be reduced. If the resistance were to be reduced by the use of a low-resistivity material for the collector, the breakdown voltage of the transistor would also be reduced, and the collector/base capacitance would be increased, both undesirable effects. To overcome these effects an epitaxial layer is employed in the collector. This is a layer, approximately 0.1 mm thick, of high-resistivity material that is deposited on the main collector and that permits the collector to be made from a material of low resistivity.

A high-power transistor will be required to conduct a large current and to be able to withstand a large collector-emitter voltage. These requirements introduce certain problems with the basic fabrication method and have led to the introduction of techniques which involve the use of two, or more, epitaxial layers.

Manufacturer's Data Sheets

Information about the ratings and the characteristics of a transistor are given by the manufacturer in the form of a **data sheet**. The data is given by quoting typical figures for the various parameters.

A number of symbols are used in data sheets with a system of subscripts that indicate the transistor terminals to which each symbol refers. The first symbol denotes the terminal at which the current or voltage is measured. The second subscript indicates which of the other two terminals is the reference terminal. A third subscript, when present, is either O, S, or R; it indicates that the third terminal is, respectively, open-circuit, short-circuit, or has a specified value of resistance connected between the third terminal and the reference terminal. Thus, V_{CEO} indicates the collector-emitter voltage with the base open-circuited, V_{CES} indicates the collector-emitter voltage with the base short-circuited to the emitter.

I_{BM}, I_{CM}, and I_{EM} are the maximum permissible values of the base, collector and emitter currents.

Some of the data that is given in a data sheet refers to parameters and characteristics that are beyond the scope of this book, e.g. data on noise performance and on thermal characteristics. These will be omitted from the simplified data sheet which follows. A data sheet has a heading that states the number of the device and which type of transistor it is. The main intended application for the transistor is also stated. A number of characteristics then follow. These include (i) transfer characteristic, (ii) h_{FE} plotted to base of I_C, (iii) f_t plotted to base of I_C, (iv) I_C plotted against $V_{CE(SAT)}$, (v) h_{ie} plotted against I_C, (vi) h_{fe} plotted against I_C, and (vii) h_{oe} plotted against I_C.

Component distributors provide the more important data in a somewhat more compact form which makes it easier for the potential user to compare the parameters of different types of transistor. The data is presented in the manner shown by Table 3.2 (p. 53).

Selection of a Transistor

The main points to be considered in the choice of a particular type of transistor are its intended application, that is, whether the device is to be operated as an amplifier or as a switch, the frequency of operation, and the currents, voltages, and powers that it will have to be able to handle.

In general, a small-signal low-frequency transistor will work satisfactorily as either an amplifier or as a switch provided that the collector current is small. The same transistor would not, however, be able to dissipate high power or have a low saturation voltage when the collector current is high.

(1) If a transistor is required for a small-signal audio-frequency amplifier, the only parameters of importance will be the current gain and perhaps the collector—base voltage. This is because the powers involved will be small enough to be handled easily by any transistor and high-frequency operation is not required. In most cases the transistor voltages are unlikely to be an important factor since the voltages in the amplifier will probably be well within the capabilities

BC 147 Silicon Planar Epitaxial Transistor
Quick Reference Data

$V_{CES(max)}$	50 V	$V_{CEO(max)}$	45 V	$I_{CM(max)}$	200 mA
$P_{tot(max)}(T_{amb} \leq 25°C)$	350 mW	$T_{J(max)}$	125°C	h_{fe}	125–500
f_t	300 MHz				

Ratings

$V_{CBO(max)}$	50 V	$V_{CES(max)}$	50 V	$V_{CEO(max)}$	45 V
$V_{EBO(max)}$	6 V	$I_{C(max)}$	100 mA	$I_{CM(max)}$	200 mA
$I_{EM(max)}$	200 mA	$I_{BM(max)}$	200 mA	$P_{tot(max)}$	350 mW
				$(T_{amb} \leq 25°C)$	

Electrical Characteristics
(T = 25°C unless otherwise stated)

I_{CBO} V_{CB} = 20 V, I_E = 0	15 nA (max.)	—	—
V_{BE} I_C = 2.0 mA, V_{CE} = 5.0 V	550 mV (min.)	620 mV (typ.)	700 mV (max)
I_C = 10 mA, V_{CE} = 5.0 V	—	—	770 mV (max)
$V_{CE(SAT)}$ I_C = 10 mA, I_B = 0.5 mA	—	90 mV (typ.)	250 mV (max)
I_C = 100 mA, I_B = 5.0 mA	—	200 mV (typ.)	600 mV (max)
$V_{BE(SAT)}$ I_C = 10 mA, I_B = 0.5 mA	—	700 mV (typ.)	—
I_C = 100 mA, I_B = 5.0 mA	—	900 mV (typ.)	—
h_{FE} I_C = 10 mA, V_{CE} = 5.0 V	40 (min.)	90 (typ.)	—
I_C = 2 mA, V_{CE} = 5.0 V	110 (min.)	180 (typ.)	220 (max)

h parameters (I_C = 2.0 mA, V_{CE} = 5.0 V, f = 1000 Hz)

h_{ie} (input impedance)	1600 Ω (min.)	2700 Ω (typ.)	4500 Ω (max)
h_{fe} (a.c. current gain)	125 (min.)	220 (typ.)	260 (max)
h_{oe} (output admittance)		18×10^{-6} S (typ.)	30×10^{-6} S (max)

of most a.f. transistors. f_t is unimportant, although it ought to be greater than the product $h_{fe} \times f_{max}$.

(2) When choosing an audio-frequency power transistor, care is necessary to ensure that the power dissipation expected within the transistor will be well within the manufacturer's quoted maximum value, and it is quite likely that the maximum collector–base voltage will also need careful consideration.

(3) A transistor selected for use in a radio-frequency amplifier should have an f_t that is several times higher than the highest frequency of operation. Then, suitable current, voltage, and power ratings can be taken into account.

(4) A transistor chosen for a switching application should have a low collector saturation voltage; usually, a general-purpose device will suffice unless a large current is to be switched. If so a specific medium-current switching transistor must be employed. If high-speed switching is required the turn-on and turn-off times will need consideration.

Table 3.2

A. Small-signal low-frequency n-p-n transistors

Type no.	V_{CEO} (V) (max)	V_{CBO} (V) (max)	V_{EBO} (V) (max)	I_C (mA) (max)	$V_{CE(SAT)}$ (V)	P_{tot} (mW) (max)	Typ. h_{FE} at I_C	Typ. f_t (MHz)
BC107	45	50	6	100	0.25	300	290 at 2 mA	300
BC108	20	30	5	100	0.25	300	520 at 2 mA	300
BC147	45	50	6	200	0.25	220	180 at 2 mA	300

B. Medium-power low-frequency n-p-n transistors

Type no.	V_{CEO}	V_{CBO}	V_{EBO}	I_C	$V_{CE(SAT)}$	P_{tot}	Typ. h_{FE} at I_C	Typ. f_t
BC142	60	80	5	800	1.0	800	20 at 200 mA	40
BC337	200	250	5	100	1.0	800	60 at 30 mA	80
BFY51	30	60	6	1000	0.35	800	40 at 150 mA	50

C. High-power low-frequency n-p-n transistors

Type no.	V_{CEO}	V_{CBO}	V_{EBO}	I_C	$V_{CE(SAT)}$	P_{tot}	Typ. h_{FE} at I_C	Typ. f_t
BD131	45	70	6	3000	—	1500	40 at 500 mA	60
BD135	45	45	5	1000	0.6	8000	100 at 150 mA	250
TIP31A	60	60	5	3000	—	40 W	25 at 3 A	3

D. Small-signal high-frequency n-p-n transistors

Type no.	V_{CEO}	V_{CBO}	V_{EBO}	I_C	$V_{CE(SAT)}$	P_{tot}	Typ. h_{FE} at I_C	Typ. f_t
BF115	30	50	5	30	—	145	40 at 1 mA	230
BF180	20	30	3	20	—	150	*	675
ZTX326	12	25	—	50	—	200	20 at 25 mA	1000

E. Medium- and high-power n-p-n transistors

Type no.	V_{CEO}	V_{CBO}	V_{EBO}	I_C	$V_{CE(SAT)}$	P_{tot}	Typ. h_{FE} at I_C	Typ. f_t
BF258	250	250	5	100	—	800	25 at 30 mA	90
2N3866	30	55	4	400	—	5000	100 at 50 mA	—

F. Medium-current switching n-p-n transistors

Type no.	V_{CEO}	V_{CBO}	V_{EBO}	I_C	$V_{CE(SAT)}$	P_{tot}	Typ. h_{FE} at I_C	Typ. f_t
BFX84	60	100	6	1000	1.0	800	110 at 150 mA	50
BSX20	15	40	4	500	0.6	350	80 at 10 mA	600
2N2219	40	75	6	800	1.0	800	200 at 150 mA	250

* Gain is expressed in a different way
Note: most general-purpose small-signal transistors are also good switches, e.g. the BC108.

4 Field-effect Transistors

The field-effect transistor (fet) is a semiconductor device which can perform all of the functions of a bipolar transistor, but which operates in a fundamentally different way. There are three kinds of fet available: the junction field-effect transistor (jfet), the insulated gate field-effect transistor (igfet), and the vertical metal-oxide-silicon power field-effect transistor (vmos). The igfet is more often known as the metal-oxide-silicon field-effect transistor (mosfet). This latter term will be used throughout this book. The mosfet can be sub-divided into two classes: the enhancement type and the depletion type. All four classes of fet can be obtained in either n-channel or p-channel versions and so a total of eight different types of fet are available.

The Junction Field-effect Transistor

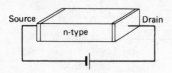

Fig. 4.1 n-type semiconductor

Fig. 4.1 shows a wafer of lightly-doped n-type silicon, provided with an ohmic contact at each of its two ends, and a battery applied between these contacts. The contact to which the positive terminal of the battery is connected is known as the **drain**, whilst the negative side of the battery is connected to the **source** contact.

A current, consisting of majority charge carriers, will flow in the silicon wafer from drain to source, the magnitude of which is inversely proportional to the resistance of the wafer. This current is known as the **drain current**. The resistance of the wafer in turn depends upon the resistivity of the n-type silicon wafer and the length and cross-sectional area of the conduction path, or *channel*, i.e. $R = \rho l/a$. For given values of resistivity and length, the channel resistance will depend upon the cross-sectional area of the channel. If, therefore, the cross-sectional area can be varied by some means, the channel resistance and hence the drain current can also be varied.

The properties of a p-n junction are such that the region either side of the junction, known as the **depletion layer**, is a region of high resistivity whose width is a function of the reverse-biased voltage applied to the junction. The depletion layer can be used to effect the

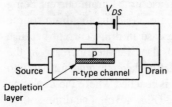

Fig. 4.2   The basic junction fet

required control of the channel resistance. A p-n junction is there-fore required in the silicon wafer and to obtain one it is necessary to diffuse a p-type region into the wafer, as shown by Fig. 4.2. The p-type region is doped more heavily than the n-type channel to ensure that the depletion layer will lie mainly within the channel. An ohmic contact is provided to the p-type region and it is known as the gate terminal.

If the gate is connected directly to the source, the p-n junction will be reverse biased and the depletion layer will be extended further into the channel. The p-n junction is reverse biased because the p-type gate region is at zero potential, while the n-type channel region is at some positive potential. A potential gradient will exist along the length of the channel, varying from a positive value equal to the bat-tery voltage at the drain end to zero voltage at the source end. Since the cross-sectional area of the channel between the gate region is smaller than at either end of the channel (because of the depletion layer), the resistance of this area is relatively large, and most of the voltage drop appears across this part of the channel. The drain end of the channel lying in between the gate region is at a higher poten-tial than the source end of the channel; hence the reverse-bias applied to the p-n junction is greater on this side. The effect on the depletion layer is shown in Fig. 4.3.

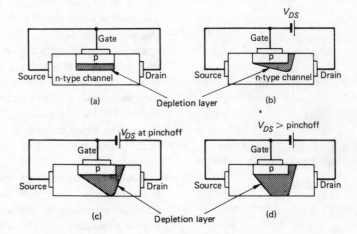

Fig. 4.3   Showing the effect of increasing the drain-source voltage

When the **drain-source voltage** is zero (Fig. 4.3a), the depletion layer either side of the p-n junction is narrow and has little effect on the channel resistance. Increasing the drain-source voltage above zero will widen the depletion layer and cause it to extend into the channel. This is shown in Fig. 4.3b which makes it clear that the layer widens more rapidly at the drain end of the channel than at the source end.

Thus, increasing the drain-source voltage increases the channel resistance and this results in the increase in the drain current being less than proportional to the voltage, i.e. doubling the drain-source voltage does not give a two-fold increase in drain current because the channel resistance has increased also. Further increase in the drain-source voltage makes the depletion layer extend further into the channel and eventually the point is reached where the depletion layer extends right across the channel (Fig. 4.3c). The drain-source voltage which produces this effect is known as the **pinch-off voltage**. Once pinch-off has developed, further increase in drain-source voltage widens the pinched-off region (Fig. 4.3d). The drain current ceases to increase in proportion to any increase in the drain-source voltage, but is now more or less constant with change in drain-source voltage. The drain current continues to flow because a relatively large electric field is set up across the depleted region of the channel, and this field aids the passage of electrons through the region.

The reverse-bias voltage applied to the gate-channel p-n junction can also be increased by the application of a negative potential, relative to source, to the gate terminal. If the **gate-source voltage** is made negative, the reverse bias on the gate-channel junction is increased. This increase in bias voltage widens the depletion layer over the width of the gate region and thereby increases the channel resistance. The drain current therefore falls as the gate-source voltage is made more negative until it is approximately equal to the pinch-off voltage and the channel is pinched-off (Fig. 4.4). When this occurs the drain current is zero. Generally, the junction fet is operated with voltages applied to both the drain and the gate terminals, with the drain voltage greater than the pinch-off value. The resistance of the channel up to the pinch-off point is determined by the gate-source voltage, and the drain-source voltage produces an electric field which sweeps electrons across the extended depletion layer. The drain current is then more or less independent of the drain-source voltage and under the control of the gate-source voltage.

A p-channel junction fet operates in a similar manner except that it is necessary to increase the gate-source voltage in the positive direction to reduce the drain current. Also, of course, the drain is held at a negative potential with respect to the source. The symbols used for n-channel, and p-channel, junction fets are given, respectively, in Figs. 4.5a and b. Both types of junction fet are operated with their gate-channel p-n junction reverse biased; hence they have a very high input impedance.

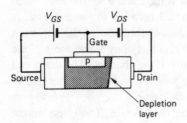

Fig. 4.4 Showing the effect of increasing the gate-source voltage

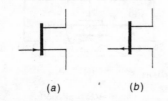

Fig. 4.5 Symbols for (a) an n-channel jfet and (b) a p-channel jfet

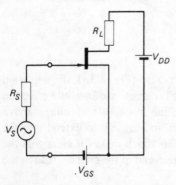

Fig. 4.6 The basic jfet amplifier

Application in an Amplifier Circuit

If a junction fet is to operate in an amplifier circuit it must be possible to control the drain current by means of the signal voltage. If the drain current is then passed through a resistance, an output voltage will be developed across the drain resistance that is an amplified version of the input signal voltage. The necessary control of the drain current can be obtained by connecting the signal voltage in the gate-source circuit of the fet (Fig. 4.6).

The signal source, of e.m.f. V_S and impedance R_S is connected in the gate-source circuit of the fet in series with a bias battery of e.m.f. V_{GS}. The total reverse bias voltage applied to the gate-channel junction is the sum of the signal voltage V_S, and the bias voltage V_{GS}. During the positive half-cycles of the signal waveform, the reverse junction bias is reduced, the depletion layer becomes narrower, and so the drain current increases. Conversely, negative half-cycles of the signal waveform augment the bias voltage and cause the depletion layer to extend further into the channel; the drain current is therefore reduced. In this way, the drain current is caused to vary with the same waveform as the input signal voltage.

The output voltage is developed across the drain load resistor R_L, and can be taken off from between the drain and earth. A voltage gain is achieved because the alternating component of the voltage across R_L is larger than the signal voltage V_S. An increase in the signal voltage in the positive direction produces an increase in the drain current and hence an increase in the voltage developed across R_L. The drain-source voltage V_{DS} is the difference between the drain supply voltage V_{DD} and the voltage across R_L; thus an increase in drain current makes the drain-source voltage fall. This means that a junction fet amplifier operated in the common-source configuration has its input and output signal waveforms in antiphase with one another. It is necessary to ensure that the signal voltage is not large enough to take the gate-source voltage positive by more than about 0.5 V, otherwise the high input-impedance feature of the junction fet will be lost.

The construction of a junction field-effect transistor is shown in Fig. 4.7g.

The various steps involved in the manufacture of an n-channel junction fet are shown by Figs. 4.7a through to g. A heavily-doped p-type silicon substrate marked as p^+ in Fig. 4.7a has a layer of silicon dioxide grown on to its surface (Fig. 4.7b). Next (Fig. 4.7c) a part of the silicon dioxide layer is etched away to create an exposed area of the p-type silicon substrate into which n-type impurities can be diffused. An n-type region is thus produced in the p-type substrate and then another layer of silicon dioxide is grown on to the surface (Fig. 4.7d). The next steps, shown by Fig. 4.7e are first to etch another gap in the silicon dioxide layer and then to diffuse a p^+ region into the exposed area of the n-type region of the substrate. A third layer of silicon dioxide is then grown over the surface of the device (Fig. 4.7f). Gaps are now etched into the layer into which aluminium contacts to the two ends of the n-type region and the upper p-type region can be deposited (Fig. 4.7g). The terminals

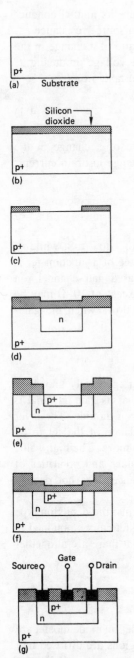

Fig. 4.7 Construction of an n-channel jfet

connected to the two ends of the n-type region are the source and the drain contacts, while the third terminal acts as the gate.

Parameters

The important parameters of a junction fet are its mutual conductance g_m, its input resistance R_{IN}, and its drain-source resistance r_{ds}. The **mutual conductance** is defined as the ratio of a change in the drain current to the change in the gate-source voltage producing it, with the drain-source voltage maintained constant, i.e.

$$g_m = \frac{\delta I_D}{\delta V_{GS}} = \frac{I_d}{V_{gs}} \quad V_{DS} \text{ constant} \tag{4.1}$$

The **drain-source resistance** r_{ds} is the ratio of a change in the drain-source voltage to the corresponding change in drain current, with the gate-source voltage held constant, i.e.

$$r_{ds} = \frac{\delta V_{DS}}{\delta I_D} = \frac{V_{ds}}{I_d} \quad V_{GS} \text{ constant} \tag{4.2}$$

Typically, g_m has a value lying in the range of 1 to 7 mS, while r_{ds} may be 40 kΩ to 1 MΩ. The **input impedance** of a junction fet is the high value presented by the reverse-biased gate-channel p-n junction. Typically, an input impedance in excess of 10^8 Ω may be anticipated. I_{DSS} is the drain current which flows when the gate-source voltage V_{GS} is zero.

The Metal-Oxide Silicon Field-effect Transistor

The metal-oxide silicon field-effect transistor, generally known as the mosfet, differs from the junction fet in that its gate terminal is insulated from the channel by a layer of silicon dioxide. The layer of silicon dioxide increases the input impedance of the fet to an extremely high value, such as 10^{10} Ω or even more. The high value of input impedance is maintained for all values and polarities of gate-source voltage, since the input impedance does not depend upon a reverse-biased p-n junction.

The mosfet is available in two different forms: the depletion type and the enhancement type. Both types of mosfet can be obtained in both n-channel and p-channel versions, so that there are altogether four different kinds of mosfet.

Depletion-type Mosfet

The constructional details of an n-channel depletion mode mosfet are shown in Fig. 4.8. Two heavily doped n^+ regions are diffused into a lightly doped p-type substrate and are joined by a relatively lightly-doped n-type channel.

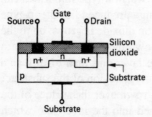

Fig. 4.8 Construction of an n-channel depletion-type mosfet

The gate terminal is an aluminium plate that is insulated from the channel by a layer of silicon dioxide. A connection is also made via another aluminium plate to the substrate itself. In most mosfets the substrate terminal is internally connected to the source terminal but sometimes an external substrate connection is made available. The substrate must always be held at a negative potential relative to the drain to ensure that the channel-substrate p-n junction is held in the reverse-biased condition. This requirement can be satisfied by connecting the substrate to the source. A depletion layer will extend some way into the channel, to a degree that depends upon the magnitude of the drain-source voltage. Because of the voltage dropped across the channel resistance by the drain current, the depletion layer extends further across the part of the channel region nearest to the drain than across the part nearest the source. The resistance of the channel depends upon the depth to which the depletion layer penetrates into the channel. With zero voltage applied to the gate terminal the drain current will, at first, increase with increase in the drain-source voltage, but once the depletion layer has extended right across the drain end of the channel the drain current becomes, more or less, constant with further increase in the drain-source voltage.

The channel resistance, and hence the drain current, of a depletion-type mosfet can also be controlled by the voltage applied to the gate. A positive voltage applied to the gate will attract electrons into the channel from the heavily-doped n^+ regions at either end. The number of free electrons available for conduction in the channel is increased and so the channel resistance is reduced. The reduction in channel resistance will, of course, allow a larger drain current to flow when a given voltage is maintained between the drain and source terminals. An increase in the positive gate voltage will increase the drain current which flows when the drain-source voltage is large enough to extend the depletion layer across the drain end of the channel. Conversely, if the gate is held at a negative potential relative to the source, electrons are repelled out of the channel into the n^+ regions. This reduces the number of free electrons which are available for conduction in the channel region and so the channel resistance is increased. The drain current that flows when the depletion layer has closed the channel depends upon the channel resistance.

The drain current of a depletion-type mosfet can therefore be controlled by the voltage applied between its gate and source terminals.

Enhancement-type Mosfet

Figure 4.9 shows the construction of an enhancement-type mosfet. The gate terminal is insulated from the channel by a layer of silicon dioxide, and the substrate and source terminals are generally connected together to maintain the channel-substrate p-n junction in the

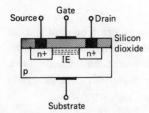

Fig. 4.9 Construction of an n-channel enhancement-type mosfet IE = Induced electrons forming a virtual channel when gate voltage is positive

reverse-biased condition. It can be seen that a channel does not exist between the n^+ source and drain regions; hence the drain current that flows when the gate-source voltage is zero is very small. If, however, a voltage is applied between the gate and source terminals, which makes the gate positive with respect to the source, a *virtual channel* will be formed. The positive gate voltage attracts electrons into the region beneath the gate to produce an n-type channel (as shown in the figure) in which a drain current is able to flow. The positive voltage that must be applied to the gate to produce the virtual channel is called the *threshold voltage* and is typically about 2 V. Once the virtual channel has been formed, the drain current which flows depends upon the magnitude of both the gate-source and drain-source voltages. An increase in the gate-source voltage above the threshold value will attract more electrons into the channel region and will therefore reduce the resistance of the channel. The drain current produces a voltage drop along the channel and as with the other types of fet, pinch-off will occur for a particular value of drain voltage. For a particular value of gate-source voltage the drain current will increase with increase in drain-source voltage up to onset of pinch-off and thereafter will remain more or less constant.

The drain current of a mosfet can hence be controlled by the voltage applied between its gate and source terminals and, if the drain current is passed through a suitable resistance, a voltage gain can be provided. The basic arrangement of a mosfet amplifier is similar to the junction fet circuit given in Fig. 4.6 and it operates in a similar manner.

The important parameters of a mosfet are the same as those of a junction fet: namely, its mutual conductance g_m, its drain-source resistance r_{ds}, and its input resistance R_{IN}. Typically, g_m is the range 1–10 mS, r_{ds} is some 5–50 kΩ, and R_{IN} is 10^{10} Ω or more. It should be noted that whereas the values of mutual conductance are approximately the same as those of a junction fet, the drain-source resistance values are lower but the input resistance is higher.

Figs. 4.10a and b show the symbols for n-channel depletion-type and enhancement-type mosfets. The symbols for the p-channel versions differ only in that the direction of the arrow-head is reversed.

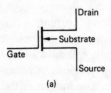

(a)

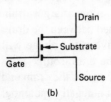

(b)

Fig. 4.10 Symbols for (a) an n-channel depletion-type mosfet and (b) an n-channel enhancement-type mosfet

Static Characteristics

The static characteristics of a fet are plots of drain current against voltage and are used to determine the drain current which flows when a particular combination of gate-source and drain-source voltages is applied. Two sets of static characteristics are generally drawn: these are the drain and the mutual characteristics.

Drain Characteristics

The **drain characteristics** of a fet are plots of drain current against drain-source voltage for constant values of gate-source voltage. The characteristics can be determined with the aid of a circuit such as

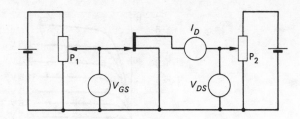

Fig. 4.11 Circuit for the determination of the static characteristics of an n-channel jfet

that shown in Fig. 4.11 for the measurement of the characteristics of an n-channel junction fet.

The data required to plot the drain characteristics consists of the values of the drain current which flows as the drain-source voltage is increased in a number of discrete steps starting from zero, the gate-source voltage being held constant at a convenient value. The method generally used to obtain the data is as follows: the gate-source voltage is set to a convenient value by means of the potential divider P_1 and then the drain-source voltage is increased, starting from zero, in a number of discrete steps. At each step the drain current flowing is noted. The gate-source voltage is then set to another convenient value and the procedure is repeated. In this way sufficient data can be obtained to plot a family of curves of drain current to a base of the drain-source voltage. This family of curves is known as the drain characteristics of the fet. The drain characteristics of the other types of fet are obtained in a similar manner. Fig. 4.12 shows typical drain characteristics for the six types of fet.

It should be noted that each curve has a region of small values of V_{DS} in which I_D is proportional to V_{DS}. In these regions the devices can be operated as a voltage-dependent resistance, i.e. as a resistance whose value V_{DS}/I_D depends upon the value of V_{DS}. For all devices the drain current which flows when the gate-source voltage is zero is labelled as I_{DSS}.

Mutual Characteristics

The **mutual or transfer characteristics** of a fet are plots of drain current against gate-source voltage for various constant values of drain-source voltage. The mutual characteristics of an n-channel junction fet can be determined using the arrangement given in Fig. 4.11 and the following procedure. The drain-source voltage is maintained at a constant value as the gate-source voltage is increased in a number of discrete steps. At each step the value of the drain current flowing is noted. The procedure should then be repeated for a number of other drain-source voltages. Typical mutual characteristics for all six types of fet are given in Fig. 4.13.

The values of the mutual conductance and the drain-source resist-

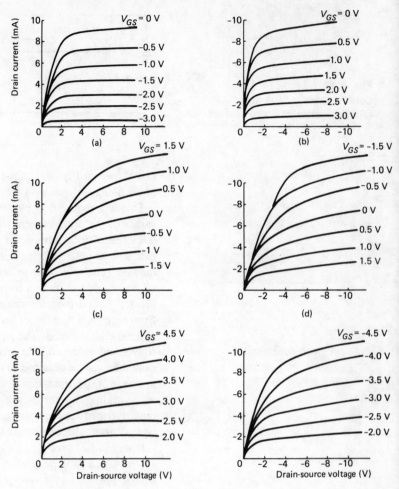

Fig. 4.12 The drain characteristic of
(a) an n-channel jfet,
(b) a p-channel jfet,
(c) an n-channel depletion type
    mosfet,
(d) a p-channel depletion type
    mosfet,
(e) an n-channel enhancement-type
    mosfet,
(f) a p-channel enhancement-type
    mosfet

[These (a)–(f) labels apply also to
Fig. 4.13]

ance can be obtained from the drain characteristics, while the mutual
conductance can be determined from the mutual characteristics. The
method employed to obtain the values of these parameters is the
same as that to determine the current gain and output resistance of
a bipolar transistor.

Example 4.1

An n-channel junction fet has the data given in Table 4.1.

Plot the drain characteristics and use them to determine the mutual conductance g_m of the device at $V_{DS}=12$ V. Calculate also the drain-source
resistance for $V_{GS} = -2$ V.

Also plot the mutual characteristics and from them obtain g_m at $V_{DS}=$
12 V.

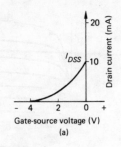

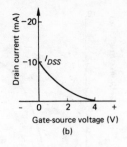

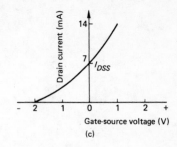

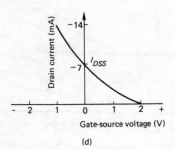

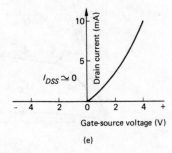

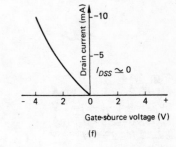

Fig. 4.13 Mutual characteristics

Table 4.1

Drain current (mA)				
Drain-source voltage V_{DS}(V)	Gate-source voltage $V_{GS} = 0$ V	$= -1$ V	$= -2$ V	$= -3$ V
0	0	0	0	0
4	7	5.0	2.4	0.30
8	10.1	5.9	2.7	0.35
12	10.2	6.2	2.9	0.40
16	10.25	6.3	3.0	0.45
20	10.3	6.35	3.05	0.50
24	10.35	6.4	3.1	0.55

Solution

The drain characteristics of the fet are shown in Fig. 4.14 (p. 64).

The mutual conductance g_m of the fet is given by the expression $g_m = \delta I_D/\delta V_{GS}$, with V_{DS} constant at 12 V. It can be seen from the characteristics that a change in V_{GS} from -2 V to -1 V produces a change in I_D from 2.9 to 6.2 mA. Therefore

$$g_m = \frac{6.2 - 2.9}{2 - 1} \times 10^{-3} = 3.3 \text{ mS} \quad (Ans.)$$

Also from the characteristics it can be seen that a change in V_{DS} from 12 to 16 V, with V_{GS} constant at -2 V, produces a change in I_D from 2.9 to 3.0 mA. Therefore

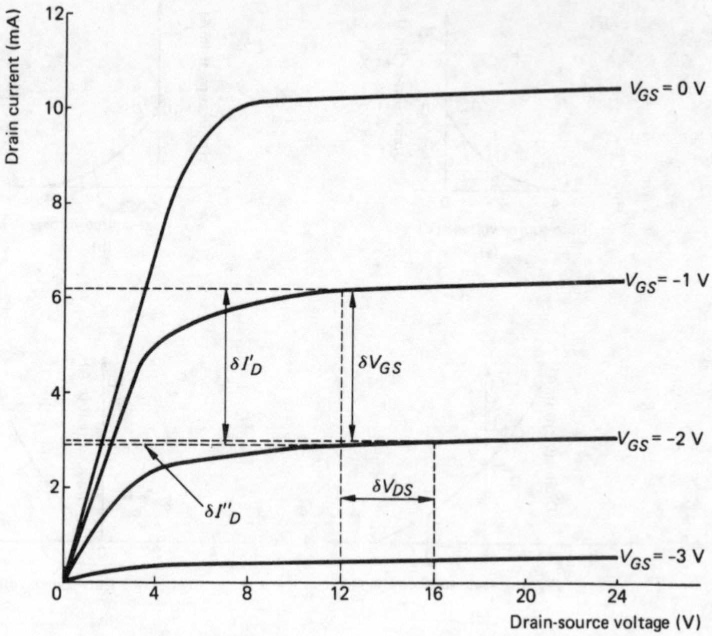

Fig. 4.14
$\delta I'_D = 6.2 - 2.9 = 3.3$ mA
$\delta V_{GS} = -1 - (-2) = 1$ V
$\delta I''_D = 3.0 - 2.9 = 0.1$ mA
$\delta V_{DS} = 8 - 2 = 6$ V

$$r_{ds} = \frac{16 - 12}{(3.0 - 2.9) \times 10^{-3}} = 40\ 000\ \Omega \quad (Ans.)$$

The mutual characteristics of the junction fet are shown plotted in Fig. 4.15. The mutual conductance g_m of the device is given by the slope of the curve; thus for V_{DS} constant at 12 V,

$$g_m = \frac{(6.2 - 2.9) \times 10^{-3}}{1} = 3.3\ \text{mS} \quad (Ans.)$$

Temperature and Frequency Effects

The velocity with which majority charge carriers travel through the channel is dependent upon both the drain-source voltage and the temperature of the fet. An increase in the temperature reduces the carrier velocity and this appears in the form of a reduction in the drain current which flows for given gate-source and drain-source voltages.

A further factor that may also affect the variation of drain current with change in temperature is the barrier potential across the gate-channel p-n junction. An increase in temperature will cause the barrier potential to fall and this, in turn, will reduce the width of the depletion layer for a given gate-source voltage. The channel resistance will fall and the drain current will increase. The two effects tend to vary the drain current in opposite directions and as a result the overall variation can be quite small. Indeed, it is possible to

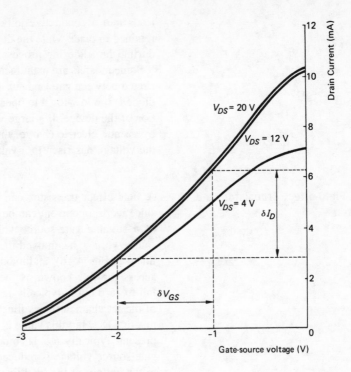

Fig. 4.15
$\delta V_{GS} = -1 - (-2) = 1$ V
$\delta I_D = 6.2 - 2.9 = 3.3$ mA

choose a particular gate-source voltage and obtain zero temperature coefficient. In general, the overall result is that the drain current decreases with increase in temperature. This is the opposite of the collector current variation experienced by the bipolar transistor. The mutual conductance of a fet will fall at high frequencies. The cut-off frequency f_c is the frequency at which g_m has fallen to 0.7 times its value at 1000 Hz.

Handling the Mosfet

The gate terminal of a mosfet is insulated from the channel by a very thin ($\simeq 100$ nm) layer of silicon dioxide, which effectively forms the dielectric of a capacitance. Any electric charge which accumulates on the gate terminal may easily produce a voltage across the dielectric that is of sufficient magnitude to break down the dielectric. Once this happens the gate is no longer insulated from the channel and the mosfet has been destroyed. The charge necessary to damage a mosfet need not be large since the capacitance between the gate and channel is very small and $V = Q/C$. This means that a dangerously high voltage can easily be produced by merely touching the gate leads with a finger or a tool. To prevent damage to mosfets in store or about to be fitted into a circuit it is usual for them to be kept with their gate and source leads short-circuited together. The protective short-circuit can be provided by twisting the leads together, by means of a springy wire clip around the leads, or by inserting the leads into a conductive jelly or grease. The short-circuit must be retained in place while the device is fitted into a circuit, particularly during the soldering process.

Some mosfets are manufactured with a Zener diode internally connected between gate and substrate. Normally, the voltage across the diode is too low for it to operate and it has little effect on the operation of the device. If a large voltage should be developed at the gate by a static electric charge, the Zener diode will break down before the voltage has risen to a value sufficiently great to cause damage.

The Field-effect Transistor as a Switch

A field-effect transistor can be employed as an electronic switch since its drain current can be turned ON or OFF by the application of a suitable gate-source voltage. In the ON condition the gate-source voltage has moved the operating point to the top of the load line (see Fig. 4.16), and maximum drain current flows. The voltage across the fet, known as the *saturation* voltage $V_{DS(SAT)}$, does not fall to zero but is typically in the range 0.2 V to 1.0 V. In the case of the fet characteristics illustrated, the ON resistance is 0.9 V/7.6 mA or 118 Ω but this value is somewhat higher than many other fets present; typically R_{ON} is some 30−200 Ω. To turn the fet OFF the gate-source voltage is reduced so that the operating point is shifted to the bottom of the load line. The drain current is now reduced to a very small value, typically 1 nA for a junction fet and about 50 pA for a mosfet.

The minimum time taken by a fet to switch from one state to the other is another important feature. Power is mainly dissipated within a fet switch during the time it is passing from one state to the other since, when the device is ON or OFF, either the voltage across it or the current in it is very small, and power dissipation is the product of voltage and current. The faster the switching speed of a fet the higher its efficiency.

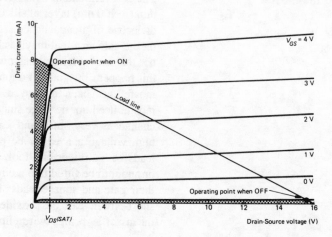

Fig. 4.16 The fet as a switch

The fet is not subject to charge storage delay as is the bipolar transistor. Limitation of the switching speed arises because of the presence of inevitable stray capacitances between both the gate-source and the drain-source terminals. The physical structure of a fet produces inter-terminal capacitances; these are the gate-drain capacitance C_{gd}, the gate-source capacitance C_{gs} and the drain-source capacitance C_{ds}. In data sheets these are represented by C_{iss}(input$=C_{gs}+C_{gd}$), C_{oss} (output$=C_{ds}$) and C_{rss} (reverse transfer $=C_{gd}$) capacitances. In determining the switching performance of a device C_{iss} is the most important factor. When an input voltage pulse is applied to a fet the input capacitance must be charged, and discharged, before V_{GS} can rise, or fall, to its final value. The lower the generator resistance the faster will be the speed of switching.

The turn-on delay time $t_{d(ON)}$ is the time required to charge the input capacitance to the gate threshold value. The risetime t_r is the time required to charge the input capacitance to a specified value above the threshold figure. The turn-off time $t_{d(OFF)}$ is the time needed to discharge the input capacitance from an over-drive voltage to the saturated gate-source voltage. The falltime t_f is the time taken by the gate voltage to fall from the saturated value to the threshold value, and for the output capacitance to charge up to the supply voltage.

Typically, $t_{d(ON)}=15$ ns, $t_r=50$ ns, $t_{d(OFF)}=90$ ns, and $t_f=50$ ns.

Power Mosfets

A power mosfet is an n-channel or a p-channel device that is capable of handling a large drain current at a high drain-source voltage and that is particularly suited to both fast switching of large currents and to audio-/radio-frequency power amplification.

Originally, power mosfets were all **vertical structure metal oxide silicon power field effect transistor** or vmosfet devices but now other types are also available. These are known as double-diffused dmosfets or tmosfets.

Vmosfets

Fig. 4.17 shows the construction of an n-channel vmosfet. It differs from the other types of fet mainly in the characteristic V-shaped groove and the positioning of the drain terminal at the bottom of the device. The gate terminal is insulated from the rest of the fet by a layer of silicon dioxide or of quartz. The source and drain terminals are placed on opposite sides of the structure so that any flow of drain current is *vertically* from drain to source. This is to be contrasted with the current flow in the jfet and in the mosfet in which current flows horizontally.

A channel does not exist between the drain and the source until a potential is applied to the gate terminal to make it positive with

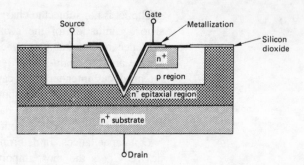

Fig. 4.17 Vmosfet

respect to the source. Then, electrons will be attracted to beneath the two surfaces of the V-shaped groove to induce a channel between the source terminal and the n^- region. Current is then able to flow from the drain to the epitaxial region and thence through the induced channel to the source terminal. The channel is of shorter length than in the more conventional fets and this reduces both the ON resistance and the self-capacitances of the vmosfet.

The p-n junctions between the p region and the two n regions are reverse biased and results in a depletion region that lies mainly in the n^- region. The presence of this high-resistance region gives the vmosfet a high value of drain-source breakdown voltage. Typical drain and mutual characteristics for a vmosfet are given in Fig. 4.18. They can be seen to be of similar shape to those for the jfet and mosfet but involve much larger currents and voltages.

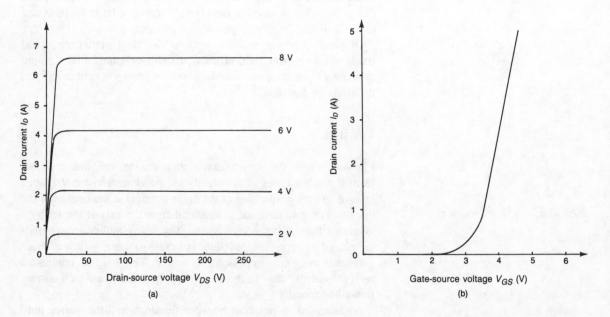

Fig. 4.18 (a) Drain and (b) mutual characteristics of a vmosfet

A number of advantages are claimed for the vmosfet over the other types. These include:

(*a*) the current density can be much larger;

(*b*) the self-capacitances are smaller;

(*c*) the ON resistance is very much smaller, typical values being some 2 to 10 ohms;

(*d*) partly because of (*a*) and partly because the construction allows the drain to be connected to a heat sink, the power dissipation of a vmosfet can be much larger; and

(*e*) the switching speed is much faster, typical turn-on and turn-off times being 4 ns each.

P-channel vmosfets are also available although perhaps are not as commonly used.

Dmosfets and Tmosfets

The V-shaped groove in the vmosfet causes a large electric field to be produced within the fet that has a tendency to break down the insulating layer at the tip of the groove. This is sometimes partially overcome by the use of a flat-bottomed groove but also by employing the alternative construction that is shown by Fig. 4.19.

Effectively, two mosfets are connected in parallel and have a common drain terminal. The source *cells*, which are hexagonal in shape for the dmosfet and of square shape for the tmosfet, are isolated from each other and from the common drain by the p regions. When the gate is made positive relative to the source enough electrons are attracted into the p-type regions to alter them to be n-type. The source cells are then no longer isolated from the drain and a drain current is able to flow to each source cell. Fig. 4.19 has shown only two source cells but a practical device would employ many thousands of them.

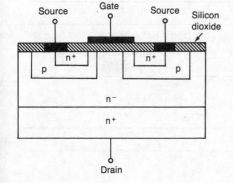

Fig. 4.19 Dmosfet

Data Sheets

The symbols employed in fet data sheets follow the same system as that used with bipolar transistors (p. 70). In addition, graphs are given of (*a*) drain current plotted to a base of drain-source voltage, (*b*) drain current against gate-source voltage, (*c*) g_m against frequency, and a few others which are beyond the scope of this book.

As for the bipolar transistor, component distributors often provide fet data in a more concise form which makes it easier to select a suitable device for a particular application (Table 4.2).

The Relative Merits of Bipolar Transistors and Fets

The input impedance of a bipolar transistor depends upon the d.c. collector current it conducts under quiescent conditions, and for the majority of applications it is somewhere in the region of 1000—3000

BF245 n-channel Junction Field-effect Transistor

Quick Reference Data

$V_{DS(max)}$	30 V	$V_{GSO(max)}$ 30 V	$P_{tot(max)}$ 300 mW
I_{DSS}	(V_{DS} = 15 V; V_{GS} = 0 V) > 2 < 6.5 mA		
V_{GS}	(cut-off)	(I_D = 10 nA, V_{DS} = 15 V)	0.5 to 8 V
g_m	(V_{DS} = 15 V; V_{GS} = 0; f = 1000 Hz;		T_{amb} = 25°C) 3.0 to 6.5 S

Ratings

$V_{DS(max)}$	30 V	$V_{DGO(max)}$	30 V	$V_{GSO(max)}$	30 V
$I_{D(max)}$	25 mA	$I_{G(max)}$	10 mA	$P_{tot(max)}$	300 mW

Characteristics

V_{GS}	=	20 V;	V_{DS}	=	0 V	I_{GSS}	< 5 nA
V_{DS}	=	15 V;	V_{GS}	=	0	I_{DSS}	= 2 to 6.5 mA
I_G	=	1 μA;	V_{DS}	=	0 V	$V_{GSS(BR)}$	> 30 V
I_D	=	200 μA;	V_{DS}	=	15 V	V_{GS}	= 0.4 to 2.2 V
g_m	=	3.0	to 8.0 mS				

Table 4.2

A. *n-channel junction fets*

Type no.	$P_{tot(max)}$ (mW)	$V_{DS(max)}$ (V)	$V_{DG(max)}$ (V)	$V_{GS(max)}$ (V)	$I_{GSS(max)}$ (nA)	g_m (mS)	Max input capacitance (pF)	$I_{DSS(max)}$ (mA)
BF244	360	30	30	30	8	4.5	5	25
MPF102	200	25	25	25	2	1.6	6	20
2N3823	300	30	30	30	0.5	3.5	7	20

B. *n-channel mosfets*

BFR84	300	20	30	20	10	15	6	—
BFS28	200	20	20	50	1	13	—	—
BSV81	200	30	30	10	0.001	—	5	—

C. *Power fets*

Type no.	Type	$P_{tot(max)}$ (W)	$V_{DS(max)}$ (V)	$V_{DG(max)}$ (V)	$V_{GS(max)}$ (V)	g_m (ms)	$I_{D(max)}$ (A)	Max input capacitance (pF)
VK1010	vmos	1	60	60	15	200	0.5	50
IRF150	dmos	150	100	100	20	10	28	3000
ZVN3315	dmos	0.63	150	100	20	—	1	28

ohms. If the transistor is biased so that its quiescent collector current is only a few microamperes, an input impedance of a megohm or more can be achieved. The input impedance of a junction fet is very high, with a mosfet having an impedance which is several orders higher still. The mutual conductance of a bipolar transistor is considerably higher than the mutual conductance of a fet; this means that the bipolar transistor is capable of providing the larger voltage gain. The collector current of a bipolar transistor increases with increase in temperature and thermal runaway is a possibility unless suitable d.c. stabilization circuitry and/or heat sinks are used. The drain current of a fet decreases with increase in temperature and there is no risk of thermal instability.

When a fet is used as a switch its ON resistance is larger than the ON resistance obtainable from a transistor but the switching operation can be carried out in either direction, i.e. the drain and source terminals are interchangeable. On the other hand, the switching speed of the fet is slower than that of the bipolar transistor. This is because the ON resistance of a fet is larger than that of a bipolar transistor and so a fet is unable to charge or discharge the stray capacitances and the input capacitance of the next stage as quickly.

The power mosfet can switch at a frequency which is at least ten times higher than is achievable by the best bipolar transistors. Further, its ON resistance is low, certainly comparable with bipolar transistors.

5 Integrated Circuits

The methods used to fabricate silicon planar bipolar and field-effect transistors can be extended to allow a complete circuit to be manufactured in a single silicon chip. All the components, active and passive, which are required by the circuit are formed at the same time in a small piece of silicon, known as a **chip**, by the diffused planar process. The circuit is known as a monolithic integrated circuit because only one silicon chip is used. The use of monolithic integrated circuits has a number of advantages over discrete circuits: greatly reduced size and weight, lower costs, complex circuit functions are economically possible, e.g. pocket calculators, and greater reliability. The size and weight reductions occur because a quite complex circuit can be enclosed within a volume of comparable dimensions to those of a single transistor. The cost of an integrated circuit depends upon its complexity and the quantity manufactured, but in many cases the cost is no greater than that of one transistor.

Other types of integrated circuit, known as thin-film and thick-film circuits, are also available; with both thin-film and thick-film circuits, resistors and capacitors are fabricated by forming a suitable film on to the surface of a glass or a ceramic substrate. The components are interconnected in the required manner by means of a deposited metallic pattern. Thin film components are produced by vacuum deposition of a suitable material on to the surface of the substrate. Thick film components are produced by painting the substrate with special kinds of ink. Active components and inductors cannot be produced in this way and any such components that are necessary must be provided in discrete form, and be joined into the metallic pattern at the appropriate points. Thick- and thin-film circuits are not used to anywhere near the same extent as monolithic circuits and they will not be discussed in this book.

Integrated Circuit Components

The fabrication of an integrated circuit component is achieved by a sequential series of oxidizing, etching and diffusion, similar to that employed for the silicon planar bipolar transistor and the field-effect

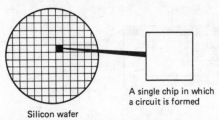

A single chip in which
a circuit is formed

Silicon wafer

Fig. 5.1 Showing how a silicon wafer is divided into a number of chips

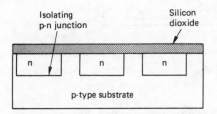

Isolating
p-n junction

Silicon
dioxide

n   n   n

p-type substrate

Fig. 5.2 Method of isolating the components in an integrated circuit

transistor (p. 49). The components that can be formed by this process are transistors, diodes, resistors and capacitors; inductors cannot be produced.

A thin wafer, about 5−10 mils* thick, is sliced from a rod of p-type silicon and will have a surface area of about 4 in^2. Since an integrated circuit may only occupy an area of about 30 mils^2, several thousands of identical circuits can be simultaneously fabricated in the one wafer. The principle is illustrated by Fig. 5.1, although to simplify the drawing fewer circuits have been shown.

Each individual silicon chip acts as a substrate into which the various components making up the circuit can be formed. The components are simultaneously formed by the diffusion of impurity elements into selected parts of the chip.

Since the p-type silicon substrate is an electrical conductor it is necessary to arrange that each of the components is insulated from the substrate. If this is not done the various components will all be coupled together by the substrate resistance. There are a number of different ways in which the required isolation can be obtained, but the most common method utilizes the high-resistance property of a reverse-biased p-n junction (see Fig. 5.2). Several n-type regions, equal in number to the number of components in the circuit, are diffused into the p-type substrate. Each of the n-type regions will be isolated from the substrate if the junction is maintained in the reverse-bias condition by connecting the substrate to a potential which is more negative than any other part of the circuit.

The various components making up the circuit are fabricated by means of a number of n-type and p-type regions which are diffused into the isolated regions. Once formed, the components are interconnected as required by the circuit by means of an aluminium pattern deposited on to the surface of the chip.

Integrated Bipolar Transistor

The most commonly used active device in a linear integrated circuit is the n-p-n bipolar transistor, the construction of which is shown in Fig. 5.3. (n$^+$ denotes a region of greater conductivity.) The construction is similar to that of the silicon planar transistor, but differs from it in that the collector contact is brought out at the top of the transistor instead of at the bottom. The change in the position of the collector contact is necessary because the collector current cannot be allowed to flow in the substrate. The collector current must therefore flow in the narrow collector region and so the device has a greater collector resistance than the discrete transistor. This, undesirable, series resistance can be minimized by the use of a buried layer. The

* One mil is one thousandth of an inch.

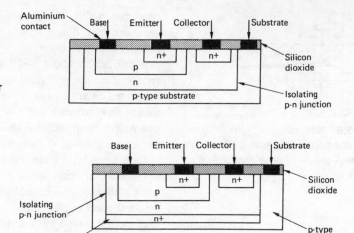

Fig. 5.3 An integrated n-p-n bipolar transistor

Fig. 5.4 An integrated n-p-n bipolar transistor with a buried layer

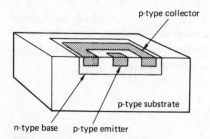

Fig. 5.5 Lateral p-n-p bipolar transistor

buried layer consists of an n^+ low-resistance region diffused into the chip in the position shown in Fig. 5.4. The buried layer is effectively in parallel with the collector region and reduces the collector series resistance. The series resistance cannot be reduced by using a lower resistivity collector region since this would reduce the breakdown voltage of the collector-base junction. Typically, an h_{fe} value of about 100 is achieved. At high frequencies, the capacitance of the isolating p-n junction may possess a sufficiently low reactance to couple the collector to the substrate and adversely affect the frequency response.

The fabrication of a p-n-p transistor is not as simple or as cheap because additional p-type and n-type regions are required. Alternatively, a different and less efficient layout known as a *lateral transistor* can be employed which is more expensive and provides a lower current gain of about 5 (see Fig. 5.5). Because of the difficulties associated with the use of the p-n-p transistor, its use in an integrated circuit is avoided whenever possible.

Integrated Mosfet

Most of the mosfets employed in digital ICs are n-channel enhancement mode devices. Depletion-mode mosfets are not often used and when they are they are generally connected to act as a resistor. P-channel mosfets are mainly used in with n-channel devices to form complementary pairs in a logic family known as **cmos**.

The fabrication of an n-channel integrated mosfet is shown by Fig. 5.6. The mosfet has an advantage over the bipolar transistor in that it is self-isolating; the drain and source regions are each isolated from

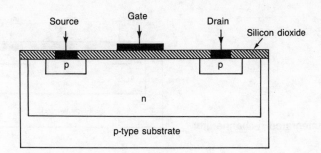

Fig. 5.6 Integrated n-channel enhancement-mode mosfet

the substrate by their individual p-n junctions, while the gate terminal is isolated by a layer of silicon dioxide. This feature allows a mosfet to be formed in a smaller area of the chip than can be achieved with a bipolar transistor. Because of this mosfets are employed in all ICs that include a large number, perhaps many thousands, of transistors. Also, required resistance and capacitance values, if not too large, are often provided by a mosfet, capacitance by a reverse-biased junction, resistance by connecting the drain to the gate.

Fig. 5.7 shows how a pair of mosfets, one an n-channel and the other a p-channel device, are formed within a cmos IC. The n-channel fets are formed within a p-type isolation region. The p^+ and n^+ regions, labelled as *stops*, are necessary to avoid an unwanted channel being induced between adjacent transistors. Because of the need to insert these stops a cmos IC occupies a greater chip area than do either pmos or nmos ICs.

Recent developments in fabrication techniques have led to the introduction of **high-speed cmos**. This uses alternative methods of fabrication that reduce the area occupied and increase the speed of operation.

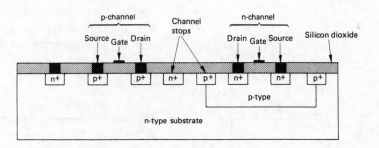

Fig. 5.7 Cmos construction

Integrated Junction Fet

The junction field-effect transistor is mainly used in some linear integrated circuits for its high input impedance. Fig. 5.8 shows the construction of an integrated n-channel jfet.

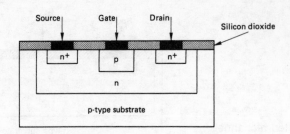

Fig. 5.8 Integrated n-channel jfet

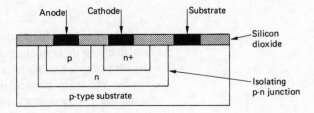

Fig. 5.9 An integrated diode

Integrated Diode

Fig. 5.9 shows the construction of an integrated circuit diode. The diode is formed at the same time as one of the junctions of a transistor and consists of a p-type region (the anode) and an n-type region (the cathode). An n^+ region is diffused into the chip to reduce the resistance of the cathode contact.

Integrated Resistor

Integrated resistors are made using a thin layer of p-type silicon that is diffused at the same time as the base of the transistor. The resistance of a silicon layer depends upon the length l, area a and resistivity ρ, of the layer according to equation (5.1), i.e.

$$R = \frac{\rho l}{a} \tag{5.1}$$

The area a of the layer is the product of the width W and the depth, d of the layer. Thus

$$R = \rho l/Wd \ \Omega$$

It is usual to express the resistance in terms of the resistance of a square of the silicon layer (Fig. 5.10) in which the width W of the layer is equal to the length l. Then, equation (5.1) can be written as

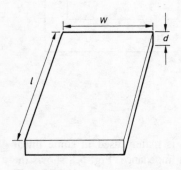

Fig. 5.10

$$R = \frac{\rho l}{ld} = \frac{\rho}{d} \ \Omega/\square \tag{5.2}$$

The resistance is now the resistance between the opposite sides of a square and it is measured in a unit known as the ohm per square. The resistance depends only upon the resistivity of the silicon layer and not upon the dimensions of the square. The resistivity of the layer is determined by the number of charge carriers (holes) that are diffused into the layer and the depth to which they penetrate. However, since both of these variables are fixed by the requirements of the simultaneously diffused transistors, a required resistance value must be obtained by a suitable choice of the length and width of the resistive path. The resistance value given by a square can be increased by increasing the length of the path. Difficulties are experienced with the fabrication of very high values of resistance because of the relatively large chip area such resistances demand.

The constructional details of an integrated resistor are given in Figs. 5.11a and b. Fig. 5.11a shows that the resistive path is formed by a p-type region that joins together the resistor contacts. A p-type path is used since it will be diffused at the same time as transistor base regions and will therefore be only lightly doped. The resistivity will therefore be in the range of $100-300$ $\Omega/\square$. When very low values of resistance are required an n-type resistor is employed; the n-type path is diffused at the same time as the transistor emitter regions and will therefore be of much lower resistivity. Fig. 5.11b shows the top view of an integrated resistor and indicates how a required resistance value may be obtained by connecting in series a number of 'squares'. The resistor can follow any path that will best utilize the surface area of the chip. The practical range of resistance values is from about 15 Ω to about 30 kΩ.

Example 5.1

The resistivity of a p-type region is 100 $\Omega/\square$. Calculate the resistance of a strip which is 1 mil wide and (i) 20 mils long, (ii) 30 mils long.

Solution
Since the resistive strip is 1 mil wide it will have a resistance of 100 Ω per 1 mil length.

(i) The resistance of a 20 mil length is $20 \times 100 = 2000$ Ω (*Ans.*)
(ii) The resistance of a 30 mil length is $30 \times 100 = 3000$ Ω (*Ans.*)

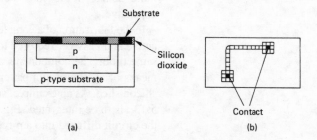

Fig. 5.11 (*a*) Side and (*b*) top views of an integrated resistor

Integrated Capacitor

Integrated capacitors can be fabricated in two ways: either the capacitance of a reverse-biased p-n junction can be utilized, or the capacitance can be provided by a layer of silicon dioxide separating two conducting areas. The construction of a junction-type capacitor is shown in Fig. 5.12a. The p-n junction is formed at the same time as either the emitter-base or the collector-base junction of a transistor. Provided the p-n junction is held in the reverse-biased condition, a capacitance of about 0.2 pF/mil can be obtained. Since the area of the chip available for a capacitor is limited, values of up to about 100 pF are available. Fig. 5.12b shows a mos capacitor; one electrode of the capacitor is provided by an aluminium layer that is deposited on to the top of the silicon layer and the other electrode is produced by the diffused n^+ region. The capacitance provided depends upon the thickness of the silicon dioxide layer and the area of the aluminium plate; up to a few hundred picofarads can be achieved.

The mos capacitor is more expensive to provide but has the following advantages over the junction capacitor: it can have voltages of either polarity applied to it, it has lower losses and a larger breakdown voltage, and its capacitance value does not depend upon the magnitude of the voltage applied across the capacitor.

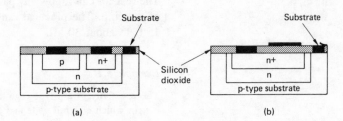

Fig. 5.12 (a) Integrated capacitor and (b) integrated mos capacitor

The Fabrication of a Complete Integrated Circuit

The main differences between integrated and discrete circuits which perform the same function are that the IC uses transistors and diodes as liberally as possible. This is because resistors and capacitors occupy more space in the chip than transistors and are therefore more expensive.

In the fabrication of a complete integrated circuit all the components, active and passive, required to make up the circuit are formed at the same time. The components are then interconnected as required by means of an aluminium pattern which is deposited on the top of the silicon slice. As an example, suppose the simple circuit shown in Fig. 5.13a is to be integrated. Fig. 5.13b shows the three components of the circuit diffused into a p-type substrate. The components are each

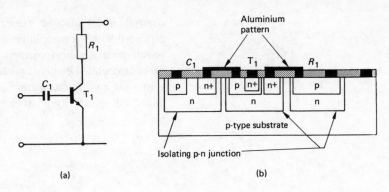

Fig. 5.13 Showing (*a*) a simple transistor circuit and (*b*) the same circuit in integrated form

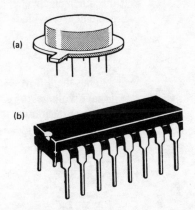

Fig. 5.14 (*a*) TO and (*b*) dil packages

isolated from the substrate by a reverse-biased p-n junction and are connected together in the required manner by an aluminium pattern which is deposited on to the surface of the chip.

A large number of circuits are simultaneously produced in a single silicon wafer, and after formation they are separated into individual chips and then sealed within a suitable package. The majority of integrated circuits are available in one or more of two kinds of package; these packages are the TO circular packages and the dual-in-line (dil). The two packages are illustrated by Figs. 5.14*a* and *b*, the latter being much the more popular.

Most ICs are either **linear** or **analogue**, circuits, or they are **digital** circuits. A linear circuit is one in which the input and output signals can vary over a *continuous* range of values. Linear ICs include audio power amplifiers, operational amplifiers (op-amps), and various radio and television circuits. Nearly all linear ICs employ bipolar transistors although a few types of op-amp have either jfet or mosfet input stages. Digital ICs operate with signals that are binary in nature, i.e. that are always in one or the other of two possible logic states, namely binary 1 or binary 0. Digital ICs include gates, counters, memories and microprocessors. The majority of digital ICs are members of either the transistor-transistor or **ttl** logic family or the complementary metal-oxide-silicon or **cmos** logic family. The former employs bipolar transistors while the latter uses mosfets.

When a linear integrated circuit is used in an equipment, a number of additional external components are also required. Operational amplifiers must have external resistors connected between the appropriate terminals to specify the overall voltage gain of the circuit, and sometimes one or more external capacitors are needed to ensure stability. Decoupling capacitors when needed must also be provided externally since the values required are too large to be fabricated in the silicon chip. The power supplies to an operational amplifier are normally decoupled while audio amplifiers require emitter decoupling capacitors. Variable resistors, such as volume and tone controls, must also be externally provided. Inductors cannot be produced within a monolithic integrated circuit and hence the desired selectivity of a radio-frequency amplifier must be specified by external components. Usually, a parallel-resonant tuned circuit is connected across the appropriate terminals for this purpose, but some circuits utilize the selectivity characteristics of ceramic or crystal filters.

6 Small-signal Audio-frequency Amplifiers

Principles of Operation

The active device used in an amplifier may be a bipolar transistor or a field-effect transistor. For brevity, in the remainder of this chapter the bipolar transistor will be referred to as a *transistor*, and the field-effect transistor as a *fet*.

Transistors and fets may be used as amplifiers because their output currents can be controlled by an a.c. signal applied to their input terminals. If a voltage or power output is required the output current must be passed through a resistive load. A fet has such a high input impedance that its input current is negligible; it can therefore give only a voltage gain. The input impedance of a transistor depends upon the magnitude of the collector current it is passing and can be made fairly large if the circuit is biased so that the collector current is only a few microamperes. By suitable choice of collector current, and hence of input impedance, a transistor may be considered as either a current- or a voltage-operated device. If the source impedance is much larger than the input impedance of the transistor, the transistor is current operated; if much smaller, it is voltage operated. For reasons given later, an audio-frequency transistor is usually operated in the common-emitter connection, when its short-circuit a.c. current gain is $h_{fe} = I_c/I_b$. The collector current is then equal to $h_{fe}I_b$. Alternatively, the a.c. collector current may be expressed in terms of the mutual conductance, g_m, of the transistor, i.e.

$$I_c = g_m V_{be}$$

This equation is valid over a wide range of collector currents, and over a frequency range from zero (direct current) to about 1 MHz.

Voltage operation of a transistor provides the advantage that less noise is introduced. Current operation gives a greater stage gain and, because a larger collector current is employed, a larger maximum permissible output signal. Voltage operation is generally restricted to the input stage of an amplifier.

The mutual characteristics of a fet or a transistor always exhibit some non-linearity. If a suitable operating point is chosen and the amplitude of the input signal is limited, the operation of the circuit may be taken as linear without the introduction of undue error.

The function of a *small-signal amplifier* is to supply a current or voltage to a load, the power output being unimportant. In a *large-signal amplifier*, on the other hand, the power output is the important factor and to obtain an adequate power output the output current and voltage swings must cover most of the characteristics.

Choice of Configuration

The various ways in which a transistor or fet may be connected to provide a gain are shown in Fig. 6.1.

A transistor connected as a **common-base** amplifier (Fig. 6.1c) has a short-circuit a.c. current gain h_{fb}, less than unity (typically about 0.992), a low input impedance of the order of 50 Ω, and an output impedance of about 1 MΩ. Because the current gain is less than unity, common-base stages cannot be cascaded unless transformer coupling is used. Transformers, however, have the disadvantages of being relatively costly, bulky and heavy and having a limited frequency response, particularly the miniature types used in transistor circuits.

The short-circuit a.c. current gain h_{fe} of a transistor connected in the **common-emitter** configuration (Fig. 6.1a) is much greater than the short-circuit a.c. current gain of the same transistor connected with common base, i.e. $h_{fe} = h_{fb}/(1 - h_{fb})$. Coupling of the cascaded

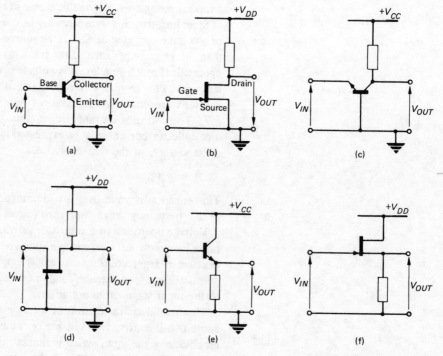

Fig. 6.1 Possible connections for transistors and fets

stages of an amplifier can be achieved without the use of a transformer. Generally, common-emitter stages are biased so that the transistor is current operated. Then the input impedance is in the region of 1000–2000 Ω while the output impedance is some 10–30 kΩ.

The **common-collector** circuit, or **emitter follower** as it is usually called, is shown in Fig. 6.1e. This connection has a high input impedance, a low output impedance, and a voltage gain less than unity. The main use of an emitter follower is as a buffer circuit that can be used to connect a high-impedance source to a low-impedance load.

In the normal mode of operation of a fet amplifier (Fig. 6.1b) the source is common to the input and output circuits, the input signal is applied to the gate, and the output is taken from between drain and earth. This connection provides a voltage gain and has a high input impedance.

Fig. 6.1f shows the fet equivalent of the emitter follower; this is known as the **source follower** circuit. Lastly, Fig. 6.1d shows the common-gate connection; this is not used at audio frequencies.

Choice of Operating Point

The mutual characteristic of a fet with a resistive drain load shows how its output current varies with change in its input voltage for a particular value of supply voltage. Similarly, the mutual characteristic of a transistor shows how the collector current of the transistor varies with change in the base-emitter voltage for a particular value of collector supply voltage.

A mutual characteristic can be used to determine, graphically, the waveform of the output current for a particular input signal waveform. Ideally, the two waveforms should be identical, but this requires the mutual characteristic to be absolutely linear. In practice, some non-linearity always exists and, for minimum signal distortion, care must be taken to restrict operation to the most linear part of the characteristic. For this a suitable **operating** or **quiescent point** must be selected and the amplitude of the input signal must be limited. The chosen operating point is fixed by the application of a steady bias voltage or current. For maximum signal handling performance the operating point is usually placed in the centre of the linear portion of the mutual characteristic. Then an alternating signal centred on this operating point produces equal swings of output current above and below the quiescent value, as shown in Figs. 6.2a and b.

The output current may conveniently be regarded as a direct current having an alternating current superimposed upon it. The direct current is equal to the current that flows when the input signal is zero, i.e. the quiescent current, and the alternating current has a peak-to-peak value of $I_{max} - I_{min}$.

The output current clearly flows at all times during a cycle of the input signal waveform. The active device is said to be operated under

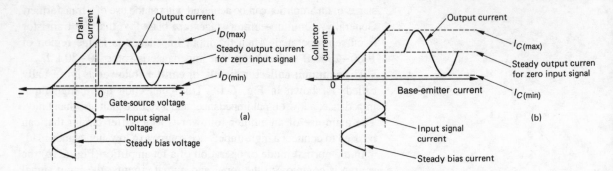

Fig. 6.2 Variations of output current with input signal for (*a*) a fet and (*b*) a transistor

Class A conditions. The peak value of the signal waveform should, at all times, be less than the bias voltage, or current, otherwise the output waveform will be distorted.

Note that Fig. 6.2*b* shows the input current as having a sinusoidal waveform; however, the relationship between the input voltage and the input current of a transistor is not a linear one unless the steady bias current is much larger than the signal current. This is because the input resistance of a transistor is not a constant quantity but varies with change in input voltage.

The selection of the operation point for a Class A amplifier depends upon a number of factors

(*a*) *Maximum output voltage*. If the maximum possible output voltage is wanted from an amplifier stage the collector-emitter voltage V_{CE} should be chosen to have a value which is approximately one-half of the collector supply voltage V_{CC}. This will position the operating point roughly half-way along the d.c. load line drawn on the output characteristics.

(*b*) *Maximum voltage gain*. To obtain the maximum voltage gain the h_{fe} of the transistor should be at, or near, its maximum value. This means (see Fig. 3.15) that the transistor should be biased to have a particular value of collector current. Also, the collector resistor should be as high as possible.

(*c*) *Minimum noise*. When noise is an important consideration the bias point must be such that the collector current is very small.

(*d*) *Battery-operated equipment*. When the circuit is a part of a battery-operated equipment a most important consideration will be keeping the current drain on the battery as low as possible.

Class B and Class C Operation

Class A operation of an amplifier offers low signal distortion. The maximum theoretical efficiency with which the d.c. power taken from the power supply is converted into a.c. signal power output is, however, only 50%, and practical efficiencies are lower than this.

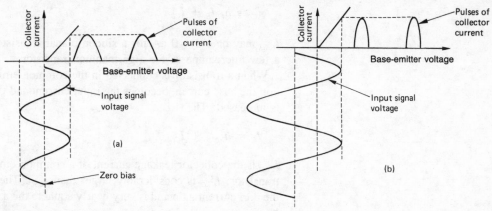

Fig. 6.3 (*a*) Class B, (*b*) Class C operation of a transistor

To obtain a greater efficiency than 50%, an amplifier may be operated under either Class B or Class C conditions.

With **Class B** operation (see Fig. 6.3*a* which refers to a transistor) the operating point is set at cut-off. The output current flows only during alternate half-cycles of the signal waveform. It is evident that the output current waveform is highly distorted; Class B bias can therefore only be used with circuits that are able to restore the missing half-cycles of the signal waveform. Such circuits are known as **push–pull** amplifiers and **tuned radio-frequency** amplifiers. Class B operation has a maximum theoretical efficiency of 78.5%.

Even greater efficiency can be obtained with **Class C** bias. With Class C bias, shown in Fig. 6.3*b*, the operating point is set well beyond cut-off. The output current flows in the form of a series of narrow pulses having a duration which is less than half the periodic time of the input signal waveform. Class C bias is used with radio-frequency power amplifiers and with some oscillator circuits. Neither Class B nor Class C bias can be used in conjunction with a resistance loaded audio-frequency amplifier, because of the excessive distortion which would then result.

Bias and Stabilization

To establish the chosen operating point it is necessary to apply a bias voltage or current to a fet or transistor.

Transistor Bias

If the current flowing into the base of a common-base connected transistor is reduced to zero, a collector current still flows. This current is produced by the passage of minority charge-carriers across the reverse-biased collector-base junction and is known as the **collector leakage current** I_{CBO}. In general, the collector current is the sum of the amplified input current and the leakage current, i.e.

$$I_C = h_{FB}I_E + I_{CBO} \tag{6.1}$$

I_{CBO} may be only 10 nA for a silicon planar transistor and perhaps a few microamperes for a germanium transistor.

When a transistor is connected in the common-emitter configuration the base current becomes the input current and the current gain is increased. Then

$$I_C = h_{FE}I_B + I_{CEO} \tag{6.2}$$

I_{CEO} is the collector leakage current of a common-emitter connected transistor; I_{CEO} is considerably larger than I_{CBO}. The quanity h_{FE} is the d.c. current gain and is very nearly equal to the a.c. current gain h_{fe}.

An increase in the temperature of the collector-base junction will produce an increase in I_{CBO}. The resulting increase in collector current gives an increase in the power dissipated at the junction, and this, in turn, increases still further the temperature of the junction and gives a further increase in I_{CBO}. The process is cumulative, and particularly in the common-emitter connection (since $I_{CEO} \gg I_{CBO}$), leads to signal distortion caused by the operating point moving along the load line. In extreme cases the eventual destruction of the transistor may occur; this is known as *thermal runaway*. To prevent thermal runaway it is often necessary to employ a bias current that also gives some degree of d.c. stabilization. The current gain h_{FE} and base-emitter voltage are also functions of temperature and can lead to changes in collector current. In addition, individual transistors of a given nominal h_{FE} may have values of h_{FE} lying between quoted maximum and minimum values. For example, one transistor's data sheet quotes h_{FE} in the range 125−500.

An amplifier stage will be designed to have a particular d.c. collector current using the nominal value of h_{FE}. The bias circuit should operate to ensure that approximately the same current will flow if a transistor using either the maximum or the minimum h_{FE} values should be used.

The simplest method of establishing the *operating point* of a common-emitter transistor is shown in Fig. 6.4. Applying Kirchhoff's second law to the circuit,

$$V_{CC} = I_B R_1 + V_{BE}$$

where V_{BE} is the base-emitter voltage. Therefore

$$R_1 = \frac{V_{CC} - V_{BE}}{I_B} \tag{6.3}$$

This circuit does not provide any d.c. stabilization against changes in collector current due to change in I_{CBO} or in h_{FE} and its usefulness is limited to 'one-off' circuits.

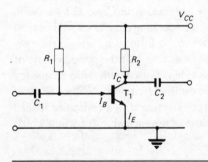

Typical values
$R_1 = 560\,\text{k}\Omega,\; R_2 = 2.7\,\text{k}\Omega$
$C_1 = C_2 = 0.47\,\mu\text{F}$

Fig. 6.4 Fixed bias

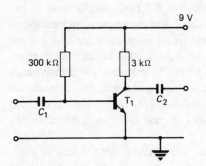

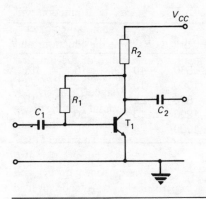

Fig. 6.5

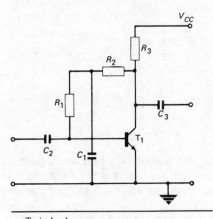

Typical values
$R_1 = 330\,\text{k}\Omega$, $R_2 = 5.6\,\text{k}\Omega$
$C_1 = 1\,\mu\text{F}$, $C_2 = 10\,\mu\text{F}$

Fig. 6.6   Collector-base bias

Typical values
$R_1 = 100\,\text{k}\Omega$, $R_2 = 220\,\text{k}\Omega$
$R_3 = 3.3\,\text{k}\Omega$, $C_1 = C_2 = C_3 = 4.7\,\mu\text{F}$

Fig. 6.7   Collector-base bias decoupled to prevent negative feedback

Example 6.1

The circuit shown in Fig. 6.5 is designed for operation with transistors having a nominal h_{FE} of 100. Calculate the collector current. If the range of possible h_{FE} values is from 50 to 160, calculate the collector current flowing if a transistor having the maximum h_{FE} is used. Assume $I_{CBO} = 10$ nA and $V_{BE} = 0.62$ V.

Solution
From equation (6.3)

$$I_B = \frac{V_{CC} - V_{BE}}{R_1} = \frac{9 - 0.62}{300 \times 10^3} = 27.9\ \mu\text{A}$$

From equation (6.2)

$$I_C = h_{FE}I_B + I_{CEO} = h_{FE}I_B + (1 + h_{FE})I_{CBO}$$
$$= (100 \times 27.9) + (101 \times 10 \times 10^{-3})\ \mu\text{A}$$

Therefore

$$I_C = 2.79\ \text{mA} \quad (Ans.)$$

Using a transistor of $h_{FE} = 160$,

$$I_C = (160 \times 27.9) + (161 \times 10 \times 10^{-3})\ \mu\text{A} = 4.46\ \text{mA} \quad (Ans.)$$

In the above example the effect of the increased collector current would be to move the operating point along the d.c. load line, and this would lead to signal distortion unless the input signal level were reduced.

A better bias arrangement, shown in Fig. 6.6, is to connect a bias resistor R_1 between the collector and base terminals of the transistor. The bias resistor R_1 provides a path for the alternating component of the collector current to feed into the base circuit. This applies *negative feedback* to the circuit and should this not be required the bias circuit is decoupled as shown in Fig. 6.7. The circuit provides some degree of d.c. stabilization against changes in the designed-for value of the collector current, the operation being briefly as follows. An increase in the collector current produces an increased voltage drop across the collector load resistor R_2. This causes the collector-emitter voltage to fall, and since this voltage is effectively applied across the base resistor R_1, the base bias current falls also. The fall in bias current leads to a fall in the collector current which to some extent compensates for the original increase.

For an improvement in the d.c. stabilization the bias arrangement of Fig. 6.8 may be employed. The base of the transistor is held at a positive potential V_B by the potential divider $(R_1 + R_2)$ connected across the collector supply $(V_B = V_{CC}R_2/R_1 + R_2)$, and the emitter is held at a positive potential V_E by the voltage developed across the emitter resistor R_4. The emitter-base bias potential is the difference between V_B and V_E, and the resistor values are chosen so that the junction is forward biased by a fraction of a volt. A base bias current

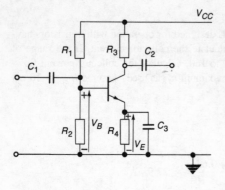

Fig. 6.8 Potential-divider bias

is therefore provided. If *negative feedback* is not wanted, the emitter resistor R_4 is decoupled by capacitor C_3. D.C. stabilization of the collector current is achieved in the following manner: an increase in the d.c. collector current, caused by an increase in the temperature of the collector-base junction, is accompanied by an almost equal increase in the emitter current. This results in an increase in the voltage V_E developed across the emitter resistor, and this in turn reduces the forward bias of the emitter-base junction. The base current is reduced causing a decrease in the collector current that compensates for the original increase.

Table 6.1 gives other possible sets of component values as alternatives to those given in Fig. 6.8.

Table 6.1

R_1(kΩ)	R_2(kΩ)	R_3(kΩ)	R_4(Ω)	C_1(μF)	C_2(μF)	C_3(μF)
68	15	2.2	560	10	10	100
120	33	3.3	1000	10	22	47
47	8.2	3.3	820	22	22	100
82	20	3.8	1200	10	50	10
100	18	4.7	1200	4.7	10	22

Example 6.2

In Fig. 6.8 the collector supply voltage V_{CC} is 12 V and the collector current I_C is 1.24 mA. Calculate (*a*) V_{CE} and (*b*) V_{BE}.

Solution
(*a*) $V_{CE} = V_{CC} - I_C R_4 - I_C R_3$
$\qquad = 12 - 1.24 \times 10^{-3} (3300 + 1000)$
$\qquad = 12 - 5.33 = 6.67$ V (*Ans.*)
(*b*) $V_E = I_C R_4 = 1.24 \times 10^{-3} \times 1000 = 1.24$ V
$\qquad V_B = V_{CC} \times R_2/(R_1 + R_2) = 12 \times 15/(15 + 82) = 1.86$ V

Therefore,

$\qquad V_{BE} = 1.86 - 1.24 = 0.62$ V (*Ans.*)

Example 6.3

A circuit of the type shown in Fig. 6.8 has the component values given in the bottom row of Table 6.1. If the collector current I_C is 1.4 mA and V_{CE} = 5 V calculate (*a*) the collector supply voltage V_{CC}, and (*b*) the power dissipated in R_3.

Solution
(*a*) $V_{CC} = V_{CE} + I_C (R_3 + R_4)$
$\qquad = 5 + 1.4 \times 10^{-3} (1200 + 3800) = 12$ V (*Ans.*)
(*b*) $P = I_C^2 R_3 = 1.4^2 \times 10^{-6} \times 3800 = 7.45$ mW (*Ans.*)

Input coupling capacitor C_1 is required to prevent the base bias current being affected by the resistance of the source. The function of the coupling capacitor C_2 is to prevent current taken from the collector supply flowing into the load. The values of C_1 and C_2 are chosen to ensure that they have negligible reactance at most of the frequencies at which the circuit is to operate. At the lower frequencies the reactances of C_1 and C_2 will become greater, and increasingly some of the signal voltage will be dropped across them. This means that the voltage gain of the circuit falls with decrease in frequency at those low frequencies at which the reactances of C_1 and C_2 are not negligibly small.

The increased reactance of decoupling capacitor C_3 at low frequencies will mean the emitter resistor R_4 is decoupled inadequately. This will allow some *negative feedback* to develop and still further reduce the gain.

The gain at high frequencies will decrease with increase in frequency because of unavoidable circuit capacitances which effectively shunt the signal path. Further loss of gain will occur if the current gain of the transistor falls with increase in frequency, but this effect can be easily avoided by choosing a transistor with a sufficiently high f_t. The gain/frequency characteristic of an audio-frequency amplifier is shown in Fig. 6.9. It can be seen that the gain is constant over a wide frequency band and falls at both low and high frequencies. The *bandwidth* of an amplifier is the band of frequencies over which the gain is not less than $1/\sqrt{2}$ times the maximum gain.

Fig. 6.9 Gain/frequency characteristic of an audio-frequency amplifier

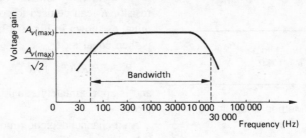

Fet Bias

The drain characteristics shown in Fig. 4.12 show that a junction fet is conducting when the gate-source voltage V_{GS} is zero. The simplest method of biasing an n-channel junction fet is therefore that given in Fig. 6.10, the disadvantages are (*a*) the maximum input signal amplitude must be very small if excessive distortion is to be avoided, and (*b*) no stabilization against changes in the d.c. drain current is provided.

Normally the n-channel junction fet is operated with its gate biased negatively with respect to its source. This can be achieved by the circuit shown in Fig. 6.11. Resistor R_1 connects the gate to the earth

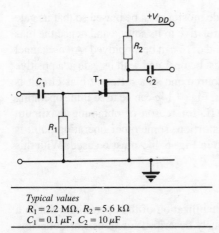

Typical values
$R_1 = 2.2\ M\Omega,\ R_2 = 5.6\ k\Omega$
$C_1 = 0.1\ \mu F,\ C_2 = 10\ \mu F$

Fig. 6.10 Junction fet simple bias

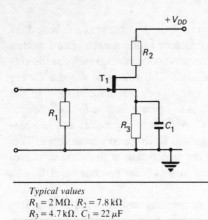

Typical values
$R_1 = 2\,\text{M}\Omega$. $R_2 = 7.8\,\text{k}\Omega$
$R_3 = 4.7\,\text{k}\Omega$. $C_1 = 22\,\mu\text{F}$

Fig. 6.11 Junction fet and depletion-type mosfet source bias

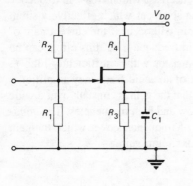

Typical values
$R_1 = 56\,\text{k}\Omega$, $R_2 = 120\,\text{k}\Omega$,
$R_3 = 1\,\text{k}\Omega$, $R_4 = 4.7\,\text{k}\Omega$,
$C_1 = 22\,\mu\text{F}$

Fig. 6.12 Method of biasing a jfet

line and the voltage drop across R_3 provides the required bias voltage. The gate current is minute and hence, for values of R_1 of a megohm or so, the direct voltage developed across R_1 is negligibly small. Resistor R_3 is often decoupled by means of capacitor C_1 to prevent negative feedback of the signal. This arrangement provides adequate d.c. stability for most small-signal stages provided that the temperature variation is not greater than about 20°C from room temperature. Junction fets of the same type are subject to wide spreads in some of their parameters and it may therefore often be necessary to use the more effective bias circuit of Fig. 6.12, which operates in similar fashion to the circuit shown in Fig. 6.8.

Improved stabilization of the drain current can be achieved if another resistor R_2 is connected between the drain supply voltage and the gate terminal (Fig. 6.12). R_1 and R_2 form a potential divider across the drain supply voltage to keep the gate potential constant. The gate-source voltage V_{GS} is the difference between the potentials of the gate and the source. If the drain current should increase for some reason, the voltage across R_3 will increase and this will make the gate potential more negative relative to the source potential. V_{GS} will be more negative and the drain current will fall, tending to compensate for the original increase.

If the junction of the bias resistors R_1 and R_2 is directly connected to the gate terminal of the fet then, at all signal frequencies, the resistors will effectively appear in parallel with the input terminals of the device. The high input impedance of the fet will then be reduced to a considerably smaller value. To minimize this shunting effect, resistor R_3 can be used to connect the bias resistors to the gate terminal as shown in Fig. 6.13. The input impedance of the amplifier is then equal to

$$R_3 + R_1 R_2/(R_1 + R_2)$$

and is approximately equal to R_3 since R_3 is chosen to be 1 MΩ or more.

An n-channel depletion-mode mosfet must be biased so that its gate is held at a negative potential relative to its source and hence the bias circuits shown in Figs. 6.12 and 6.13 can be employed. An n-channel enhancement-mode mosfet must be operated with its gate at a positive potential with respect to its source and so a different bias circuit is necessary. The circuit shown in Fig. 6.14a can be used if the operating point $V_{GS} = V_{DS}$ is suitable. If, for reason of obtaining maximum output voltage or minizing distortion, some other operating point is required then the circuit given in Fig. 6.14b must be used. With this circuit

$$V_{GS} = V_{DS} R_2/(R_1 + R_2)$$

Both circuits provide d.c. stabilization of the operating point in a similar manner to that previously described for transistor collector-base bias.

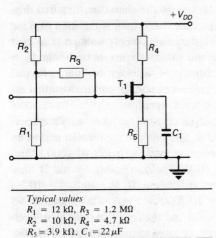

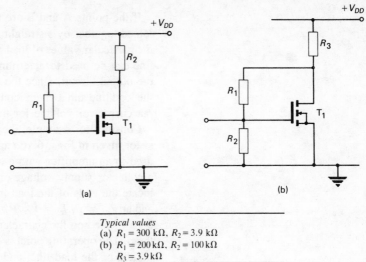

Typical values
$R_1 = 12\ k\Omega,\ R_3 = 1.2\ M\Omega$
$R_2 = 10\ k\Omega,\ R_4 = 4.7\ k\Omega$
$R_5 = 3.9\ k\Omega,\ C_1 = 22\ \mu F$

Fig. 6.13 Junction fet and depletion-type mosfet potential-divider bias

Typical values
(a) $R_1 = 300\ k\Omega,\ R_2 = 3.9\ k\Omega$
(b) $R_1 = 200\ k\Omega,\ R_2 = 100\ k\Omega$
   $R_3 = 3.9\ k\Omega$

Fig. 6.14 Enhancement-type mosfet bias

Determination of Gain using a Load Line

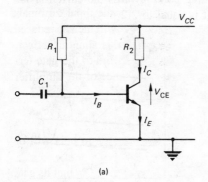

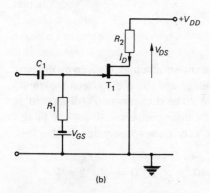

Fig. 6.15 Currents and voltages in basic amplifiers

The voltage gain of a fet amplifier or the current gain of a transistor amplifier can be determined with the aid of a 'load line' drawn on the output current/output voltage characteristics of the device. The currents and voltages existing in the collector or drain circuit of a simple resistance-loaded amplifier are shown in Figs. 6.15a and b respectively. In each of these circuits the d.c. collector or drain current flows in the load resistor R_2 and develops a voltage across it. The direct voltage which is applied across the transistor or fet is equal to the supply voltage minus the d.c. load voltage.

Thus, referring to Fig. 6.15,

$$V_{CE} = V_{CC} - I_C R_2 \qquad (6.4)$$

$$V_{DS} = V_{DD} - I_D R_2 \qquad (6.5)$$

Equations (6.4) and (6.5) are of the form $y = mx + c$ and are therefore equations to a straight line. In order to draw a straight line it is only necessary to plot two points; these points can best be determined in the following manner. Point A: Let $I_C = I_D = 0$ in equations (6.4) and (6.5) respectively, then,

$$V_{CE} = V_{CC} \quad \text{and} \quad V_{DS} = V_{DD}$$

Point B: Let $V_{CE} = V_{DS} = 0$ in equations (6.4) and (6.5) respectively, then

$$0 = V_{CC} - I_C R_2 \quad \text{or} \quad I_C = \frac{V_{CC}}{R_2}$$

$$0 = V_{DD} - I_D R_2 \quad \text{or} \quad I_D = \frac{V_{DD}}{R_2}$$

If the points A and B are marked on the characteristics and then joined together by a straight line, the line drawn is the **load line** for the particular values of load resistance and supply voltage. The load line can be used to determine the values of current and voltage in the output circuit, since the ordinate of the point of intersection of the load line and a given input current or voltage curve gives the output current or voltage for that input signal.

Consider for example, the output characteristics of an n-p-n transistor given in Figs. 6.16a and b, and suppose the transistor is to be used in an amplifier with a collector load resistance of 2000 Ω and a collector supply voltage of 10 V. The two points, A and B, that locate the ends of the load line are at $I_C = 0$, $V_{CE} = V_{CC} = 10$ V, and at $V_{CE} = 0$, $I_C = V_{CC}/R_2 = 10/2000 = 5$ mA. These points have been located on the characteristics and the load line drawn between them. The operating point is often chosen to lie approximately in the middle of the load line, and has been selected as the point marked P. The required base bias current is then equal to 20 μA. The d.c. collector-emitter voltage ($V_{CE} = V_{CC} - I_C R_2$) is found by projecting vertically downwards from the operating point to the voltage axis. This step is shown by a dashed line in Fig. 6.16a and it determines the standing (or quiescent) collector-emitter voltage as 5.6 V. Similarly, the d.c. collector current which flows is found by projecting horizontally from the operating point towards the current axis. Thus, the d.c. collector current is equal to 2.2 mA.

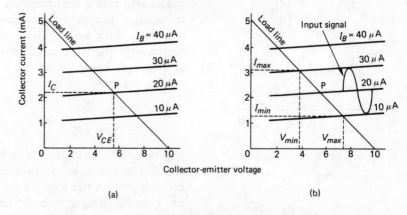

Fig. 6.16

(a)   (b)

The d.c. power taken from the collector supply is given by the product of the collector supply voltage and the d.c. collector current, i.e. $10 \times 2.2 \times 10^{-3} = 22$ mW. The **d.c. power** P_C dissipated at the collector of the transistor is the difference between the d.c. power supplied to the circuit and the d.c. power dissipated in the load resistance. Hence,

$$P_C = 22 \times 10^{-3} - (2.2 \times 10^{-3})^2 \times 2000 = 12.32 \text{ mW}$$

P_C is also equal to the product of the d.c. collector current and the quiescent collector-emitter voltage; thus,

$$P_C = 2.2 \times 10^{-3} \times 5.6 = 12.32 \text{ mW}$$

The load line can also be used to find the variation in collector current and collector-emitter voltage which is produced by the application of a signal to the base of the transistor. Suppose as in Fig. 6.16b that a sinusoidal signal of peak value 10 μA is applied. This signal is superimposed upon the base bias current of 20 μA and so the base current is varied from a minimum value of 10 μA to a maximum value of 30 μA. The corresponding values of collector current and collector-emitter voltage are determined by projecting to the current and voltage axes from the points of intersection of the load line and the curves for $I_B = 10$ μA and $I_B = 30$ μA. This has been shown by the dashed lines drawn on Fig. 6.16b. The collector current is varied from a minimum value $I_{min} = 1.3$ mA to a maximum value $I_{max} = 3.25$ mA. The collector-emitter voltage is varied from a minimum value $V_{min} = 3.6$ V to a maximum value $V_{max} = 7.3$ V. The a.c. component of the collector current has a peak-to-peak value of $(3.25 - 1.3)$ mA or 1.95 mA, while the peak-to-peak value of the a.c. component of the collector-emitter voltage is $(7.3 - 3.6)$ or 3.7 V. The current gain A_i of the amplifier is

$$A_i = \frac{\text{Peak-to-peak change in collector current}}{\text{Peak-to-peak change in base current}}$$

Hence,

$$A_i = \frac{1.95 \times 10^{-3}}{20 \times 10^{-6}} = 97.5$$

Example 6.4

The transistor used in a single-stage audio-frequency amplifier with a resistance load of 2000 Ω has the data given in Table 6.2.

Plot the output characteristics of the transistor and draw the load line assuming a collector supply voltage V_{CC} of 8 V.

(i) Select a suitable operating point.
(ii) Determine the current gain A_i when an input signal producing a base

Table 6.2

| V_{CE}(V) | I_C(mA) | | | |
	$I_B = 5$ μA	$I_B = 10$ μA	$I_B = 15$ μA	$I_B = 20$ μA
2	0.85	1.55	2.32	3.08
4	1.00	1.74	2.56	3.35
6	1.13	1.92	2.76	3.60
8	1.30	2.13	3.00	3.85

current swing of 5 μA about the chosen bias current is applied to the circuit.

(iii) Assuming the input resistance of the transistor is 1900 Ω determine the voltage gain A_v.

(iv) Calculate the power gain A_p.

Solution

The output characteristics are shown plotted in Fig. 6.17. The d.c. load line must be drawn between the points

$$I_C = 0, \quad V_{CE} = V_{CC} = 8 \text{ V}, \quad \text{and}$$
$$V_{CE} = 0, \quad I_C = V_{CC}/R_2 = 8/2000 = 4 \text{ mA}$$

(i) Since the input signal has a peak value of ± 5 μA a suitable base bias current is 10 μA, the operating point is then P.

(ii) When a signal of ± 5 μA peak is applied to the transistor, the base current varies between 5 μA and 15 μA. Projection from the intersection of the load line and the 5 μA and 15 μA base current curves to the current axes gives the resulting values of collector current as 1.15 mA and 2.45 mA.

The peak-peak collector current swing is therefore 2.45 – 1.15 or 1.30 mA and the current gain is

$$A_i = \frac{1.3 \times 10^{-3}}{10 \times 10^{-6}} = 130 \quad (Ans.)$$

(iii) If the input resistance of the transistor is 1900 Ω the a.c. voltage applied to the transistor must be

$$\pm 5 \times 10^{-6} \times 1900 \quad \text{or} \quad \pm 9.5 \times 10^{-3} \text{ V}$$

Projecting from the intersection of the load line and the appropriate base current curves to the voltage axis gives the peak-peak collector voltage as

$$5.7 - 3.08 = 2.62 \text{ V}$$

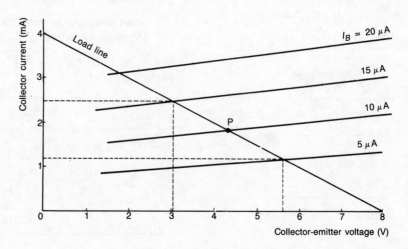

Fig. 6.17

Voltage gain $A_v = \dfrac{2.62}{19 \times 10^{-3}} = 138$ (*Ans.*)

Alternatively, using equation (3.7),

$$A_v = \frac{A_i R_L}{h_{ie}} = \frac{130 \times 2000}{1900} = 137 \quad (Ans.)$$

(iv) The power output of the transistor is the product of the r.m.s. values of the a.c. components of the collector current and the collector-emitter voltage. Therefore

$$\text{Output power} = \frac{\text{peak-peak } I_c}{2\sqrt{2}} \times \frac{\text{peak-peak } V_{ce}}{2\sqrt{2}}$$

$$= \tfrac{1}{8}[(I_{c(max)} - I_{c(min)}) \ (V_{ce(max)} - V_{ce(min)})]$$

$$= \tfrac{1}{8}(1.3 \times 10^{-3} \times 2.62) = 4.258 \times 10^{-4} \text{ W} \quad (Ans.)$$

The input power delivered to the transistor is

$$I^2_{b(rms)} h_{ie} = \left(\frac{5 \times 10^{-6}}{\sqrt{2}}\right)^2 \times 1900 = 23.75 \times 10^{-9} \text{ W}$$

Power gain $A_p = P_{out}/P_{in} = 4.258 \times 10^{-4}/23.75 \times 10^{-9} = 17\ 928$

(*Ans.*)

Alternatively using equation (3.8)

$$A_p = A_i^2 R_2/h_{ie} = A_i A_v = 130 \times 137 = 17\ 810 \quad (Ans.)$$

Example 6.5

Determine the mutual conductance of the transistor in Example 6.4. Use this value to calculate the voltage gain of the circuit.

Solution

$g_m = h_{fe}/h_{ie} = 130/1900 = 68.4 \text{ mS}$ (*Ans.*)
or, $g_m = 38 \times 10^{-3} \times I_c = 38 \times 10^{-3} \times 1.8 = 68.4 \text{ mS}$ (*Ans.*)
Voltage gain $= g_m R_L = 68.4 \times 10^{-3} \times 2 \times 10^3 = 137$ (*Ans.*)

Since the mutual conductance g_m is primarily determined by the d.c. collector current its value is more predictable than is the value of h_{fe} and so g_m is increasingly employed in performance calculations.

A.C. Load Lines

Very often the load into which the transistor or fet works is not the same for both a.c. and d.c. conditions. When this is the case two load lines must be drawn on the characteristics: a d.c. load line to determine the operating point, and an **a.c. load line** to determine the current or voltage gain of the circuit. The a.c. load line *must* pass through the operating point.

Fig. 6.18 shows the circuit of a single-stage common-emitter

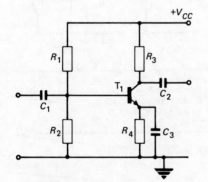

Typical values
$R_1 = 56 \text{ k}\Omega, \ R_2 = 10 \text{ k}\Omega$
$R_3 = 3 \text{ k}\Omega. \ R_4 = 1 \text{ k}\Omega$
$C_1 = C_2 = 10 \ \mu\text{F}$
$C_3 = 47 \ \mu\text{F}$

Fig. 6.18 A single-stage common-emitter amplifier

amplifier using potential-divider bias. The emitter decoupling capacitor C_3 has a very high reactance at very low frequencies and does not shunt the emitter resistance R_4 at zero frequency (direct current). The d.c. load on the transistor is therefore $R_3 + R_4$ ohms. At signal frequencies the reactance of C_3 is low and the a.c. load on the transistor is reduced to R_3 ohms. A d.c. load line is first drawn on the output characteristics between the points

$$I_C = 0, \quad V_{CE} = V_{CC}, \quad \text{and}$$
$$V_{CE} = 0, \quad I_C = V_{CC}/(R_3 + R_4)$$

(see Fig. 6.19). A suitable operating point P is then selected.

The a.c. load line must be drawn passing through the operating point with a slope equal to the reciprocal of the a.c. load on the transistor, i.e. $-1/R_3$. To avoid extending the current axis, proceed as follows. (*a*) Assume that the a.c. load is actually a d.c. load, and using any convenient value of supply voltage (V_1 in Fig. 6.19), draw lightly the corresponding d.c. load line using the method previously explained, i.e. between points V_1 and V_1/R_3. (*b*) This load line has the required slope, so draw the actual a.c. load line parallel to it and passing through the operating point.

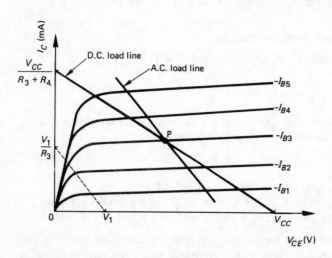

Fig. 6.19 A.C. and d.c. load lines

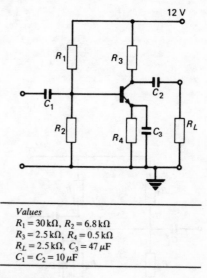

Values
$R_1 = 30\,k\Omega, \ R_2 = 6.8\,k\Omega$
$R_3 = 2.5\,k\Omega, \ R_4 = 0.5\,k\Omega$
$R_L = 2.5\,k\Omega, \ C_3 = 47\,\mu F$
$C_1 = C_2 = 10\,\mu F$

Fig. 6.20

Example 6.6

The transistor used in the circuit of Fig. 6.20 has the data given in Table 6.3. Plot the output characteristics of the transistor, draw the d.c. load line and select a suitable operating point. Draw the a.c. load line and use it to find the a.c. voltage across the 2500 Ω load R_L when an input signal V_{be} of peak value 15 mV is applied to the circuit. Assume all the capacitors have zero reactance at signal frequencies.

Table 6.3

V_{CE}(V)	$V_{BE}=610$ mV	$V_{BE}=620$ mV	$V_{BE}=630$ mV	$V_{BE}=640$ mV
		I_C(mA)		
3	0.85	1.55	2.32	3.08
5	1.00	1.74	2.56	3.35
7	1.13	1.92	2.76	3.60
9	1.30	2.13	3.00	

Solution

The output characteristics are shown plotted in Fig. 6.21. The d.c. load on the transistor is $R_3 + R_4 = 3000$ Ω; the d.c. load line must therefore be drawn between the points

$$I_C = 0, \quad V_{CE} = 12 \text{ V} \quad \text{and}$$
$$V_{CE} = 0, \quad I_C = 12/3000 = 4 \text{ mA}$$

Since the input signal has a peak value of 15 mV, a suitable base bias voltage is 625 mV, the operating point is then P.

The a.c. load on the transistor is the 2500 Ω collector resistor in parallel with the 2500 Ω load, i.e. 1250 Ω. An a.c. load line with a slope of $-1/1250$ must therefore be drawn. To draw a d.c. load line with the same slope assume a convenient supply voltage, say 5 V; then this d.c. load line joins the points

$$V_{CE} = 5 \text{ V} \quad \text{and} \quad I_C = 5/1250 = 4 \text{ mA}$$

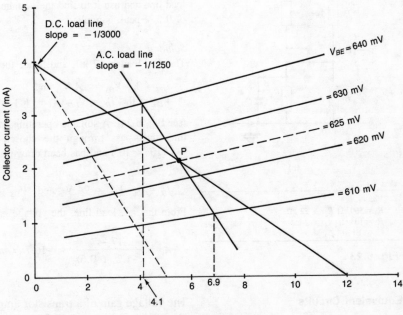

Fig. 6.21

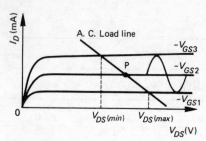

Fig. 6.22 Use of a.c. load line to calculate the voltage gain of a fet amplifier

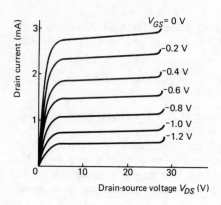

(a)

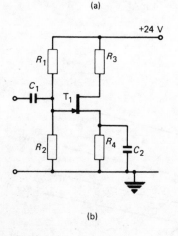

(b)

Values
$R_1 = 560\,k\Omega, R_2 = 22\,k\Omega$
$R_3 = 10\,k\Omega, R_4 = 2\,k\Omega$
$C_1 = 0.1\,\mu F, C_2 = 4.7\,\mu F$

Fig. 6.23

Equivalent Circuits

The equivalent d.c. load line is shown dotted and the wanted a.c. load line has been drawn parallel to it and passing through the operating point.

When a signal of ± 15 mV (peak) is applied to the transistor V_{BE} varies between 610 mV and 640 mV. Projection from the intersection of the load line and the 610 mV and 640 mV V_{BE} curves gives the resulting values of collector voltage as 4.1 V and 6.9 V. The peak collector signal voltage is therefore (6.9 – 4.1)/2 or 1.4 V.

Voltage Gain of Fet Amplifier

The **voltage gain of a fet** can also be found with the aid of a load line. For example, Fig. 6.22 shows an a.c. load line drawn on the drain characteristics of a fet, and the dotted projections from the load line shown how the drain voltage swing, resulting from the application of an input signal voltage, can be found. The voltage gain A_v of the fet amplifier stage is

$$A_v = \frac{\text{Peak-to-peak drain voltage}}{\text{Peak-to-peak gate-source voltage}} \tag{6.6a}$$

$$= \frac{V_{DS(max)} - V_{DS(min)}}{V_{GS3} - V_{GS1}} \tag{6.6b}$$

Example 6.7

Fig. 6.23a shows the drain characteristics of a common-source n-channel junction fet, which is used in the single-stage amplifier circuit shown at (b). Draw the d.c. load line and select a suitable operating point. Draw the a.c. load line and use it to find the voltage gain when a sinusoidal input signal of 0.3 V peak is applied.

Solution
The d.c. load is 12 kΩ, and hence the d.c. load line must join the points

$$I_D = 0, \quad V_{DS} = 24\,V \quad \text{and}$$
$$V_{DS} = 0, \quad I_D = V_{DD}/(R_3 + R_4) = 24/(12 \times 10^3) = 2\,mA$$

(see Fig. 6.24). A suitable operating point is $V_{GS} = -0.9$ V. The a.c. load line must pass through the chosen operating point with a slope of $-1/(10 \times 10^3)$ and has been drawn parallel to the dotted line joining the points

$$I_D = 0, \quad V_{DS} = 24\,V \quad \text{and} \quad V_{DS} = 0, \quad I_D = 24/(10 \times 10^3) = 2.4\,mA$$

From the a.c. load line, the voltage gain of the circuit is

$$A_v = \frac{17 - 7}{-1.2 - (-0.6)} = -16.7 \quad (Ans.)$$

The voltage gain of a transistor amplifier can be calculated using an **equivalent circuit**, or **model**, of the transistor. An equivalent circuit

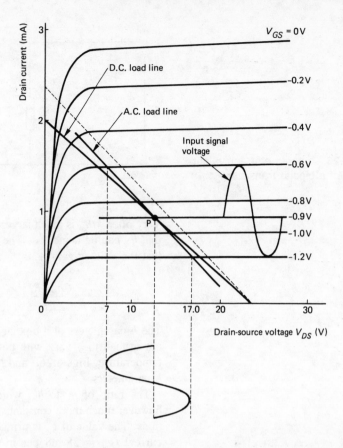

Fig. 6.24

is one that behaves in exactly the same way as the device it represents. Two circuits are often employed for audio-frequency amplifier calculations; these are the **_h_ parameter** circuit and the **mutual conductance** circuit.

_h_ Parameter Circuit

The _h_ parameter equivalent circuit of a bipolar transistor is shown by Fig. 6.25. The three _h_ parameters have been met previously in Chapter 3. h_{ie} is the input impedance with V_{CE} constant, h_{fe} is the current gain with V_{CE} constant, and h_{oe} is the output admittance with I_B constant.

When a collector load resistance R_L is connected across the output of the equivalent circuit it will appear in parallel with the output resistance $1/h_{oe}$ of the transistor. The collector current $I_c = h_{fe}I_b$ flows in the total resistance to produce the output voltage $V_{OUT} = V_{ce}$. Therefore,

$$V_{OUT} = h_{fe}I_b \times \frac{R_L \times 1/h_{oe}}{R_L + 1/h_{oe}} = h_{fe}I_bR_L^1.$$

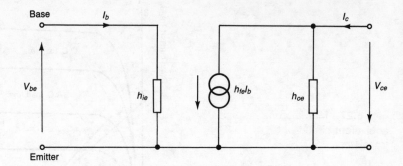

Fig. 6.25 *h* parameter equivalent circuit of a bipolar transistor

Very often $1/h_{oe}$ is much larger than R_L so that $R_L^1 \simeq R_L$ which means that h_{oe} can be neglected. The input voltage is $V_{IN} = V_{be} = I_b h_{ie}$ so that the voltage gain A_v is

$$A_v = \frac{V_{OUT}}{V_{IN}} = \frac{h_{fe} I_b R_L}{I_b h_{ie}} = \frac{h_{fe} R_L}{h_{ie}} \tag{6.7}$$

The *h* parameters of a bipolar transistor are not constant quantities but instead they vary with both the collector current and with the temperature. Figs 6.26*a* and *b* show typical variations of the three *h* parameters.

The ratio of h_{fe} to h_{ie}, which is the mutual conductance g_m, is however much more constant since h_{fe} and h_{ie} vary in different directions. The value of g_m is primarily determined by the d.c. collector current ($g_m = 38$ mS per mA of collector current) and is easily predictable. Calculations are therefore often based upon the mutual

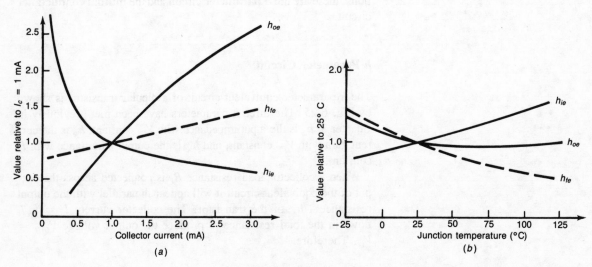

Fig. 6.26 Variation of *h* parameters with (*a*) collector current and (*b*) temperature

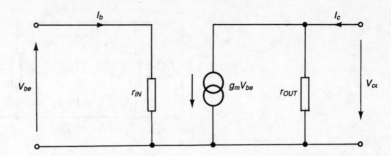

Fig. 6.27 Mutual conductance equivalent circuit of a bipolar transistor

conductance model of the transistor. This is shown by Fig. 6.27. The output resistance r_{OUT} is often omitted since its effect on the voltage gain is generally small.

Consider the circuit given in Fig. 6.28. At signal frequencies the reactances of the three capacitors are negligibly small. The collector supply line is effectively at earth potential as far as signals are concerned and so the bias resistors R_1 and R_2 are in parallel with one another and with the base-emitter terminals of the transistor. The emitter resistor R_4 is effectively short circuited and the collector resistor appears between the collector and the emitter. Thus, the equivalent circuit of the amplifier is as given in Fig. 6.29a and b.

The bias resistors shunt the signal path and so reduce the input resistance of the circuit. To limit this effect the bias resistors should be of as high a value as possible.

If the parameters of the transistor are $h_{ie} = 2000\ \Omega$ and $h_{fe} = 120$ and hence $g_m = 120/2000 = 60$ mS, then the voltage gain of the circuit is

$$A_v = V_{OUT}/V_{IN} = 120 \times 4700/2000 = 282.$$

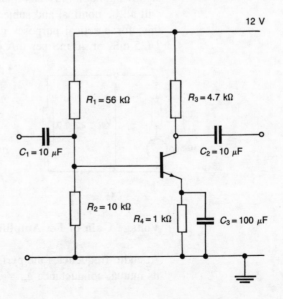

Fig. 6.28

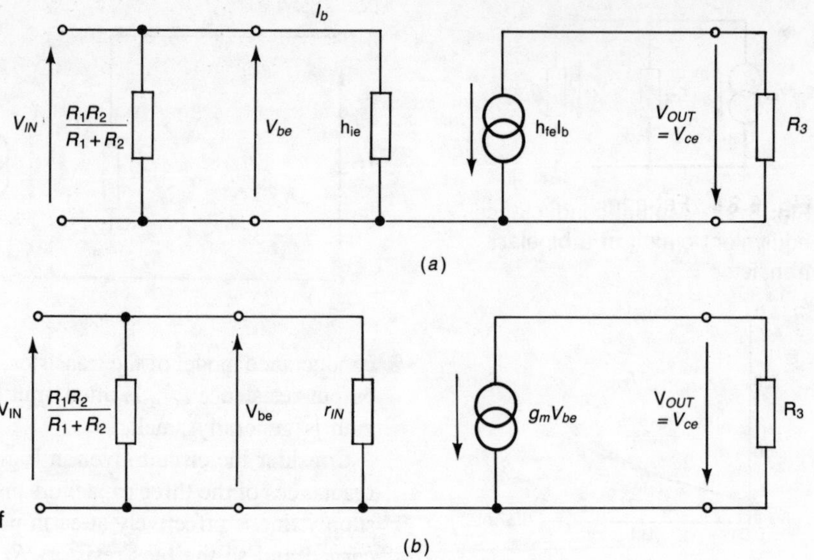

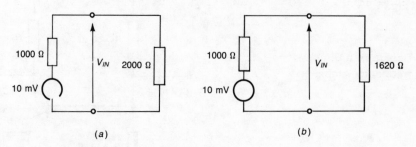

Fig. 6.29 Equivalent circuits of Fig. 6.28

(a)

(b)

The presence of the bias resistors does not affect the voltage gain of the circuit but does reduce the input voltage that appears across the input terminals. Suppose, for example, that the source has an e.m.f. of 10 mV and an internal resistance of 1000 Ω. Then, Fig. 6.30a, the input voltage is $V_{IN} = 6.67$ mV ($V_{OUT} = 1.88$ V) if the bias resistors are neglected. If, Fig. 6.30b, the bias resistors are taken into account, the input resistance of the amplifier r_{IN} is found from $1/r_{IN} = 1/2000 + 1/(56 \times 10^3) + 1/(10 \times 10^3)$ and $r_{IN} = 1620$ Ω. Now the input voltage is 6.18 mV ($V_{OUT} = 1.74$ V).

The difference between the two output voltages obtained may seem significant but it must be remembered that the quoted resistor values will all be nominal and subject to tolerance variations. Because of this, for practical purposes g_m is usually taken as being equal to $I_C/25$ mS, or 40 mS per mA of collector current.

Fig. 6.30

(a)

(b)

Voltage Gain of Fet Amplifier

At audio-frequencies the performance of a fet can be described by its mutual conductance $g_m = I_d/V_{gs}$, where I_d and V_{gs} are a.c. com-

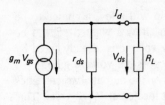

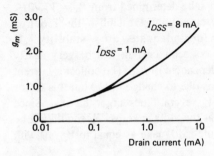

Fig. 6.31 Fet equivalent circuit

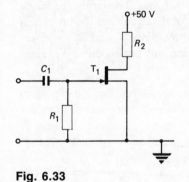

Fig. 6.32 Variation of fet mutual conductance with drain current

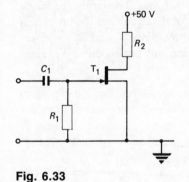

Fig. 6.33

Design of a Single-stage Audio-frequency Amplifier

ponents, and the equivalent circuit of Fig. 6.31. The resistance r_{ds} is the output resistance of the device and is equal to $\delta V_{DS}/\delta I_D = V_{ds}/I_d$ with V_{GS} constant. The output voltage V_{ds} is given by

$$V_{ds} = \frac{g_m V_{gs} R_L r_{ds}}{R_L + r_{ds}}$$

Therefore the voltage gain A_v is given by

$$A_v = \frac{V_{ds}}{V_{gs}} = \frac{g_m R_L r_{ds}}{r_{ds} + R_L} \qquad (6.8)$$

If, as is usual, $r_{ds} \gg R_L$,

$$A_v = g_m R_L \qquad (6.9)$$

The mutual conductance of a fet is not constant but is a function of the drain current as shown in Fig. 6.32. As for a transistor, the operating point must be selected to give the required value of g_m. (I_{DSS} is the drain current for $V_{GS} = 0$.)

Example 6.8

Calculate the drain load resistance required to give the circuit of Fig. 6.33 a voltage gain of 20. The fet used has $g_m = 4 \times 10^{-3}$ S and $r_{ds} = 100$ kΩ.

Solution

From equation (6.8), $A_v = 20 = \dfrac{4 \times 10^{-3} \times 10^5 R_2}{10^5 + R_2}$

Therefore $R_2 = \dfrac{20 \times 10^5}{380} = 5.26$ kΩ   (*Ans.*)

Alternatively, using the approximate expression, equation (6.9)

$$A_v = 20 = 4 \times 10^{-3} R_2 \quad \text{or} \quad R_2 = \frac{20}{4 \times 10^{-3}} = 5000 \ \Omega \quad (Ans.)$$

In the design of a single-stage audio-frequency amplifier a number of factors must be taken into account. These include the choice of operating point and the required voltage gain. Other factors such as the required bandwidth and noise performance are also of importance but are beyond the scope of this book. There are several different approaches to a design available and here just one of them is given.

Suppose that the stage is to deliver the maximum possible output voltage so that the collector-emitter voltage V_{CE} will be set at one-half of the supply voltage V_{CC}. Assuming for the moment, that the rest of the supply voltage is dropped across the collector resistor R_3, then $V_{CC}/2 = I_C R_3$. The voltage gain $A_v = g_m R_3 = 40 I_C \times V_{CC}/2I_C$

$= 20V_{CC}$. This approximate relationship will allow a choice to be made of the collector supply voltage to allow a wanted gain to be obtained, or alternatively, if the supply voltage is already fixed by other considerations, will establish the possible voltage gain.

A suitable d.c. load line can be drawn on the output characteristics of the transistor and the operating point located at $V_{CC}/2$ volts. This allows the collector current to be determined. Alternatively, a collector current may be arbitrarily selected, which will very often be the value quoted in the data sheet for the typical value of h_{FE}.

The collector resistor can then be determined from $R_3 = V_{CC}/2I_C$.

The potential divider bias circuit must establish the required operating point and provide adequate d.c. stability. If $h_{FE}R_4 \gg R_1R_2/(R_1 + R_2)$ the collector current will be very nearly equal to $(V_B - V_{BE})/R_4$, i.e. independent of h_{FE}. The collector current is then still subject to variations due to change in V_{BE} but this factor may be minimized by making V_B several times larger than V_{BE}. Since $V_E = V_E + V_{BE}$ this means that the voltage across R_4 should not be less than about 1 V. A good rule is to make V_E equal to $V_{CC}/10$ with a 1 V minimum value.

For the circuit to operate correctly the base voltage V_B should remain more or less constant at $V_B = V_{CC}R_2/(R_1 + R_2)$ as the collector current and thus $V_E = I_CR_4$ varies. To achieve this the current flowing through the bias resistor R_2 must be several times larger, by a factor n, than the base current $I_B = I_C/h_{FE}$. The larger the factor n the better will be the d.c. stability of the circuit but the lower will be the values of the resistors R_1 and R_2. Since R_1 and R_2 are effectively in parallel with the signal path and with one another their values

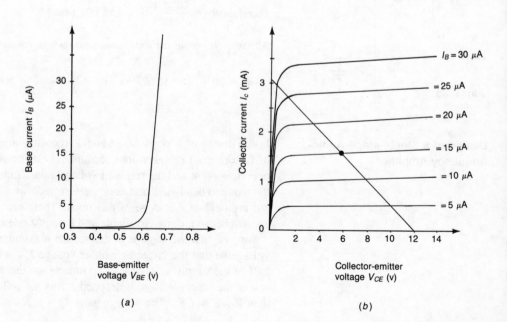

Fig. 6.34

(a)

(b)

must not be too small. This means that the choice of n must be a compromise between the a.c. and d.c. performances of the circuit. A suitable choice for n is 10.

Then, $R_2 = V_B/nI_B$ and $R_1 = (V_{CC} - V_B)/(n + 1)I_B$. Calculation of suitable values for the coupling and decoupling capacitors is more difficult and values such as those quoted in Table 6.1 should be used.

Example 6.9

Design an audio-frequency single-stage amplifier to have a voltage gain of about 240 using the transistor whose characteristics are given in Fig. 6.34. The maximum possible output voltage is required.

Solution

Voltage gain $= 240 = 20V_{CC}$, or $V_{CC} = 240/20 = 12$ V. The operating point is then set at $V_{CE} = 6$ V, $I_B = 15$ μA. The d.c. load line has been drawn through these two points. The d.c. collector current is then 1.5 mA and $h_{FE} = (1.5 \times 10^{-3})/(15 \times 10^{-6}) = 100$.

The slope of the load line is $(12 - 6)/(1.5 - 0) \times 10^{-3} = 4000$ Ω. The emitter voltage $V_E = V_{CC}/10 = 12/10 = 1.2$ V. Hence, $R_4 = 1.2/(1.5 \times 10^{-3}) = 800$ Ω. Choosing the nearest preferred values for R_3 and R_4; $R_3 = 3900$ Ω and $R_4 = 820$ Ω. Now the voltage drop across $(R_3 + R_4)$ is $1.5 \times 10^{-3} \times (3900 + 820) = 7$ V which leaves V_{CE} as 5 V.

The base current $I_B = I_C/h_{FE} = 15$ μA. Therefore, choose the current in R_2 to be 150 μA. From Fig. 6.35a, when $I_B = 15$ μA, $V_{BE} = 0.65$ V, giving $V_B = 1.2 + 0.65 = 1.85$ V. Then,

$$R_2 = \frac{1.85}{10 \times 15 \times 10^{-6}} = 12.3 \text{ k}\Omega$$

and

$$R_1 = \frac{12 - 1.85}{11 \times 15 \times 10^{-6}} = 61.5 \text{ k}\Omega$$

Choosing the nearest preferred values, $R_2 = 12$ kΩ and $R_1 = 62$ kΩ.

The midband voltage gain will be $g_m R_3 = 38 \times 1.5 \times 10^{-3} \times 3900 = 222$. To increase the gain nearer to the wanted target of 240 the next higher preferred value for R_3 could be used, i.e. $R_3 = 4300$ Ω. Then $A_v = 245$ but the maximum output voltage will be reduced.

7 Power Supplies

All electronic equipments require a power supply of some kind to provide the necessary d.c. operating voltages and currents. Some portable equipments, such as transistor radio receivers, are battery operated but the majority of equipment employs an electronic power supply. The basic power supply consists of (1) a transformer whose function is to convert the a.c. mains supply voltage to the lower value required by the equipment, (2) a rectifier unit whose function is to convert the a.c. voltage supplied by the transformer to a d.c. voltage, and (3) a filter whose purpose is to remove *ripple* from the rectified voltage.

The correct operation of many equipments demands that the direct power supply voltage is maintained at a constant value, within fairly fine limits, even though the input mains voltage and/or the current taken from the power supply may vary. Generally, the inherent regulation of a supply is inadequate to meet the demands placed upon it by the supplied equipment and then some kind of voltage stabilization circuitry must be provided. The function of a voltage stabilizer is to maintain a constant voltage across the load as the input voltage and/or the load current vary within specified limits.

Rectifier Circuits

A number of different circuits exist that are capable of converting an a.c. supply into a pulsating d.c. current and they may be broadly divided into one of two classes, half-wave rectifiers and full-wave rectifiers.

Half-wave Rectification

In its simplest form, **half-wave rectification** consists merely of the connection of a diode in series with the a.c. supply and the load, as shown in Fig. 7.1a.

The diode conducts only during those alternate half-cycles of the a.c. supply voltage V_s that make point A positive relative to point B,

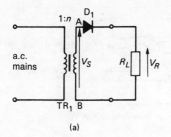

(a)

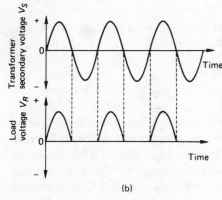

(b)

Fig. 7.1 The half-wave rectifier with resistance load

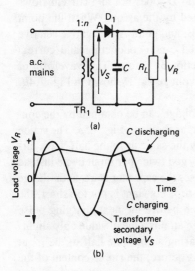

(a)

(b)

Fig. 7.2 The half-wave rectifier with resistance-capacitance load

Typical values

$R_L = 20 \ \Omega \quad C \ 1000 \ \mu F$

and so the load current consists of a series of half sine-wave pulses. The voltage V_R developed across the load is the product of the load current and the load resistance and has the same waveform as the load current (Fig. 7.1*b*). The disadvantage of this simple rectifying circuit is very clear: the load voltage, although unidirectional, varies considerably and is, indeed, zero for half the time. Such a waveform is only suitable for simple applications, such as battery charging, since the variations will appear as noise at the output of any equipment fed by the supply. When the diode is non-conducting, the peak voltage across it, known as the *peak inverse voltage* (p.i.v.), is equal to the peak value of the transformer secondary voltage. This voltage must not exceed the voltage rating of the type of diode employed.

The d.c. output of a rectifier circuit is required to be as steady as possible and a great step towards this goal could be achieved if the load voltage could be prevented from falling to zero during alternate half-cycles. One way of achieving this is to connect a capacitor C in parallel with the load as shown in Fig. 7.2*a*. Each time the diode conducts, the current that flows charges the capacitor and the voltage across the capacitor builds up. During the intervals of time when the diode is non-conducting, the capacitor discharges via the load resistance and prevents the load voltage falling to zero (Fig. 7.2*b*). The capacitor continues to discharge, at a rate determined by the time constant CR_L seconds, until the point A is taken more positive than the capacitor voltage by a positive half-cycle of the input voltage V_S. The diode then conducts, the capacitor is recharged, and the capacitor voltage rises again. If the load current is fairly small the capacitor does not discharge very much between charging pulses and the average load voltage V_R is only slightly less than the peak value of the applied voltage V_S. The p.i.v. is increased to twice the peak secondary voltage V_S because of the polarity of the voltage developed across C.

The value of the load voltage is adjustable, within limits, by suitable choice of the turns ratio n of the input transformer. An increase in the load, i.e. in the load current, means that the load resistance is less; this, in turn, means that the time constant of the discharge path is smaller. Capacitor C then discharges more rapidly and the load voltage is not as constant (see Fig. 7.3).

A completely steady load voltage cannot be obtained in this way since too large a value of capacitance would be required. The maximum value of capacitance that can be employed is limited, because the larger the capacitance value the greater the current required to charge the capacitor to a given voltage, and the current that can be handled by a diode is limited to a figure quoted by the manufacturer. The fluctuating, unidirectional voltage appearing across the load may be regarded as a d.c. voltage having an a.c. voltage superimposed upon it. This a.c. voltage is known as the **ripple voltage** and is at the frequency of the supply voltage, usually 50 Hz. The ripple voltage is undesirable, since the object of rectification is to provide a steady

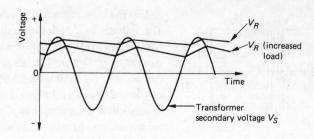

Fig. 7.3 Showing the effect of load changes on a half-wave rectifier with resistance-capacitance load

d.c. voltage, and can be removed by a smoothing or filter circuit connected between the diode and the load.

Full-wave Rectification

With **full-wave rectification** of an a.c. source, both half-cycles of the input waveform are utilized and alternate half-cycles are inverted to give a unidirectional load current. The circuit of a full-wave rectifier is shown in Fig. 7.4a and can be seen to require two diodes. The secondary winding of the input transformer TR_1 is accurately centre-tapped so that equal voltages are applied across the two diodes D_1 and D_2. During those half-cycles of the input waveform that make point A positive with respect to point B and point C negative relative to point B, D_1 conducts and D_2 does not and current flows in the load in the direction indicated by the arrow. When the point C is positive with respect to point B, and point A is negative relative to point B, D_2 is conducting and D_1 non-conducting and current flows in the load in the same direction as before. The waveform of the current, and hence of the load voltage V_R, is shown in Fig. 7.4b. The p.i.v. is $2V_S$.

A more constant value of load voltage can be obtained by the connection of a capacitor across the load as shown in Fig. 7.5a. The action of the reservoir capacitor is exactly the same as in the half-wave circuit but now the capacitor is re-charged twice per input cycle instead of only once. Between charging pulses the capacitor starts to discharge through the load but, provided the time constant is not too short, the load voltage has not fallen by much before the next charging pulse occurs (Fig. 7.5b). The load voltage attains a mean value only slightly less than the peak voltage appearing across one half of the input transformer secondary winding. As before, the ripple content of the load voltage increases with increase in load current and can be reduced by the use of a suitable filter network.

The full-wave circuit has a number of advantages over the half-wave circuit: it is more efficient; little, if any, d.c. magnetization of the transformer core occurs; and the ripple voltage is at twice the supply frequency, i.e. at 100 Hz. The increase in the ripple frequency

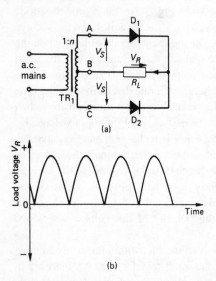

Fig. 7.4 The full-wave rectifier with resistance load

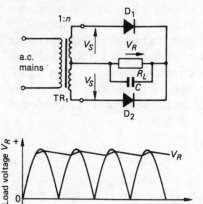

Fig. 7.5 The full-wave rectifier with resistance-capacitance load

Typical values

$R_L = 50\ \Omega \quad C = 2200\ \mu F$

makes it easier to reduce the percentage ripple to a desired level. The disadvantages of the circuit are the need for a centre-tapped transformer and for two diodes.

An alternative method of full-wave rectification is the use of a bridge network (see Fig. 7.6). The **bridge rectifier** circuit requires four diodes instead of two but avoids the need for a centre-tapped input transformer. Further, the arrangement gives a load voltage that is nearly twice as great as that from the circuit of Fig. 7.5a — assuming, of course, the same transformer secondary voltage. During those half-cycles of the input that make point A positive with respect to point B, diodes D_2 and D_4 are conducting and diodes D_1 and D_3 are non-conducting; current therefore flows from point A to point B via D_2, the load R_L, and D_4. When point A is negative relative to point B, D_1 and D_3 are conducting and D_2 and D_4 are non-conducting; current then flows from point B to point A via D_3, the load R_L, and D_1. Both currents pass through the load in the same direction and so a fluctuating, unidirectional voltage is developed across the load having the waveform of Fig. 7.4b. The variations in load voltage can be reduced by the connection of a capacitor across the load; the load voltage waveform is then that of Fig. 7.5b.

When higher d.c. voltages are required, the bridge circuit has some advantages over the circuit using a centre-tapped transformer: the p.i.v. of each diode is only equal to the peak secondary voltage V_S; a centre-tapped secondary winding is not required; and the current rating of the transformer is less. This means that a smaller and hence cheaper transformer can be used.

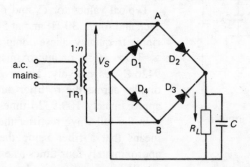

Fig. 7.6 The bridge rectifier

Typical values

$R_L = 30\ \Omega \quad C = 2200\ \mu F$

Filter Circuits

A power supply unit for electronic equipment must provide a d.c. voltage of minimum ripple content. To reduce the ripple voltage to a tolerable level it is generally necessary to include some kind of filter circuit between a rectifier and its load. The simple capacitor connected in shunt across the load reduces ripple and is, therefore, a simple filter that may be adequate for some applications. Further smoothing of the output voltage can be achieved if the capacitor is followed by either an $L-C$ or an $R-C$ network, or, alternatively, the rectifier may feed directly into a series inductor. The effectiveness of a filter can be judged in terms of the reduction in ripple voltage it gives, but another and (usually) equally important criterion is its voltage regulation. The **load regulation** of a rectifier circuit is a measure of how its output voltage changes as the current taken from it is varied. Ideally, of course, the output voltage should remain constant, so good regulation implies that the voltage changes very little as the load current is varied from minimum to maximum. The percentage regulation of a power supply is given by

$$\% \text{ regulation} = \frac{V_{no\text{-}load} - V_{full\text{-}load}}{V_{no\text{-}load}} \times 100\% \qquad (7.1)$$

The line regulation is a measure of the change in output voltage because of a change in the input voltage, with the load current held constant.

Capacitor-input Filters

A capacitor-input filter consists of a shunt capacitor, connected across the output terminals of the rectifier, followed by a basic low-pass filter. The low-pass filter may consist of a series inductor and a shunt capacitor as in Fig. 7.7, or a series resistor and a shunt capacitor as shown in Fig. 7.8. In the $L-C$ filter the value of capacitance C_1 is chosen to give a reasonably smooth output voltage from the rectifier proper, and the values of L and C_2 are chosen to give adequate ripple suppression.

Typical values for C_1 and C_2 for a half-wave rectifier are 32 μF each and for L, 30 H, and at 50 Hz, which is the half-wave rectifier ripple frequency, these components have reactances of $1/(2\pi \times 50 \times 32 \times 10^{-6})$, or approximately 100 Ω, and $2\pi \times 50 \times 30$, or 9426 Ω, respectively. The reactances of C_2 and L act as a potential divider across the rectifier output and reduce the ripple voltage to approximately 100/9326 times its original value.

In the full-wave rectifier the ripple frequency is 100 Hz and this means that a filter using the same component values would be approximately four times as efficient. For a given amount of ripple, smaller components can be used and typical values are $C_1 = C_2 = 8$ μF and $L = 15$ H. Both filters have negligible effect on the wanted d.c. component of the rectified output voltage. In order to obtain the fairly large capacitance values required cheaply and in the minimum volume, electrolytic capacitors are normally used.

The disadvantages of the capacitor-input $L-C$ filter are (a) the cost, weight, size and external fields of the series inductor, and (b) the relatively poor voltage regulation. The first of these disadvantages can be overcome by replacing the series inductor with a series resistor, although this has the obvious disadvantage of increasing the d.c. voltage drop in the filter. The $R-C$ filter, therefore, has poor regula-

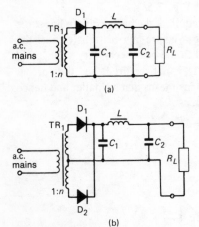

Fig. 7.7 The capacitor-input L-C filter

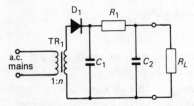

Fig. 7.8 The capacitor-input R-C filter

tion and requires adequate ventilation to conduct away the heat produced in the resistor. As a result it is only used to supply equipments taking only a small current.

The circuit of a capacitor-input $R-C$ filter is shown in Fig. 7.8, such filters are used in the power supply units of some television receivers and cathode-ray oscilloscopes. Typical values are $R = 100$ to $200\ \Omega$, $C_1 = 100\ \mu F$ and $C_2 = 150$ to $200\ \mu F$.

Choke-input Filters

When a **choke-input filter** is used there is no reservoir capacitor and the rectifier feeds directly into the filter (Fig. 7.9). Inductor L and capacitor C form a potential divider across the output of the rectifier and reduce the ripple voltage to a low value. The choke-input filter can only be used in conjunction with a full-wave rectifier since it requires current to flow at all times, the current being provided first by D_1 and then by D_2. The current waveforms in the circuit are shown in Fig. 7.10. The fact that current flows continuously, instead of in a series of pulses as in the capacitor-input filter circuits, means that the input transformer is used more efficiently. A further advantage is that the ripple content at the output of the filter is less dependent on the load current. Typical values for L are 5 to 30 H and for C, 5 to 40 μF.

Fig. 7.11 gives a comparison of the voltage regulation of the two types of filter. It can be seen that although the output voltage of the choke-input filter is the smaller, its regulation is better. The regulation can be improved by the use of a larger value of inductance as shown by the two lower curves. If the load current falls below a certain critical value I' or I'' (this could happen each time the equipment was first switched on), the output voltage will rise abruptly. To prevent this happening a resistor, known as a 'bleeder', can be connected across the output terminals of the filter to ensure that a current greater than the critical value is always taken.

As an alternative to the use of a bleeder resistor with its consequent power dissipation, a *swinging choke* can be used. This is an inductor whose inductance depends upon the magnitude of the direct current flowing in its windings. Typically, such an inductor might have an inductance of 30 H with zero current flow and only 5 H with 250 mA flowing.

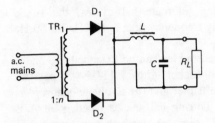

Fig. 7.9 The choke-input filter

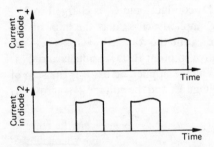

Fig. 7.10 Current waveforms in the choke-input filter

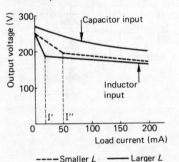

Fig. 7.11 Regulation curves for capacitor- and choke-input filters

Voltage Multiplying

The use of a suitable combination of rectifiers and capacitors can give a d.c. output voltage that is several times greater than the peak voltage appearing across the secondary winding of the input transformer. Consider, for example, Fig. 7.12 which shows a voltage-doubling circuit. During the half-cycles of the input when point A is positive with respect to point B, diode D_1 conducts and capacitor C_1 is charged to

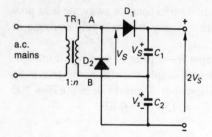

Fig. 7.12 The voltage doubler

the peak voltage V_S appearing across the secondary winding of transformer TR_1. When point B is positive relative to point A, diode D_2 conducts and capacitor C_2 is charged to the same voltage. Capacitors C_1 and C_2 are connected in series across the output terminals and so the voltage appearing across these terminals is equal to twice the peak secondary voltage, i.e. $2V_S$. If large values of capacitance are used and the load current is fairly small, the output voltage has small ripple content and good regulation. Since the capacitors are charged during alternate half-cycles, the ripple frequency is at twice the supply frequency, that is 100 Hz for 50 Hz mains.

The principle of the voltage doubler can be extended to voltage tripling, quadrupling or even higher. Fig. 7.13 shows possible arrangements for (a) a voltage tripler and (b) a voltage quadrupler. Consider the voltage tripler. During half-cycles when point A is positive with respect to point B, diode D_1 conducts and capacitor C_2 is charged to V_S volts. During the half-cycles when point B is positive relative to point A, D_2 conducts and C_1 is charged to $2V_S$ volts — because the voltage applied across it is the sum of the transformer secondary voltage V_S and the voltage V_S across C_2. Also, when point A is positive relative to point B, D_3 conducts and C_3 is charged to $3V_S$, because the voltage applied across it is the sum of the transformer secondary voltage V_S and the voltage $2V_S$ across C_1.

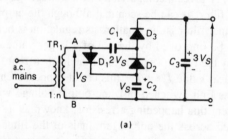

(a)

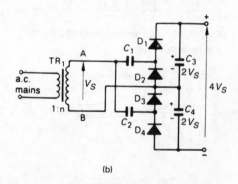

(b)

Fig. 7.13 (a) The voltage tripler and (b) the voltage quadrupler

Voltage Stabilizers

For many applications a power supply consisting of a transformer, a rectifier and a filter has an inadequate performance. Firstly, the voltage regulation is not good enough and, secondly, the d.c. output voltage varies with change in the a.c. mains voltage. To improve the constancy of the d.c. output voltage as the load and/or the a.c. input voltage vary, a voltage stabilizer circuit must be employed. The

Fig. 7.14 Block diagram of a stabilized power supply

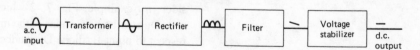

voltage stabilizer is connected between the output of the filter circuit and the load as shown in Fig. 7.14.

Zener Diode Voltage Stabilizer

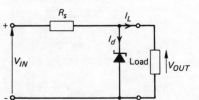

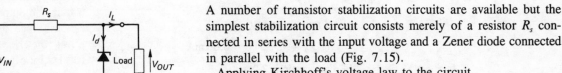

Fig. 7.15 The Zener diode stabilizer

A number of transistor stabilization circuits are available but the simplest stabilization circuit consists merely of a resistor R_s connected in series with the input voltage and a Zener diode connected in parallel with the load (Fig. 7.15).

Applying Kirchhoff's voltage law to the circuit,

$$V_{IN} = (I_d + I_L)R_s + V_{OUT}$$

Rearranging

$$R_s = \frac{V_{IN} - V_{OUT}}{I_d + I_L} \tag{7.2}$$

When a Zener diode is operated in its breakdown region, the current flowing through the diode can vary considerably with very little change in the voltage across the diode. If the load current should increase, the current through the Zener diode will fall by the same percentage in order to maintain a constant voltage drop across R_s and hence a constant output voltage. Should the load current decrease, the diode will pass an extra current such that the sum of the two currents flowing in R_s is maintained constant, and the output voltage of the circuit is *stabilized*.

The other cause of output voltage variations is change in the voltage applied across the input terminals of the circuit. If the input voltage should increase, the Zener diode will pass a larger current so that the extra voltage is dropped across R_s. Conversely, if the supply voltage falls, the diode takes a smaller current and the voltage dropped across R_s is reduced. Because of the varying voltage drop across R_s, the load voltage fluctuates to a much lesser extent than does the input voltage.

Calculation of Series Resistance

(a) Varying load; Fixed supply voltage
When the load current varies, the current taken by the diode varies by the same percentage in the opposite direction. The diode current reaches its maximum value when the load current is zero, and at this point care must be taken to ensure that the maximum power dissipation rating of the diode is not exceeded. Therefore

$$I_{d(max)} = \frac{\text{Maximum power dissipation}}{\text{Diode (output) voltage}} \tag{7.3}$$

The required value of R_s can now be calculated using equation (7.2).

Example 7.1

A Zener diode stabilizing circuit is to provide a 24 V stabilized supply to a variable load. The input voltage is 30 V and a 24 V, 400 mW Zener diode is to be used. Calculate (i) the series resistance R_s required and (ii) the diode current when the load resistance is 2000 Ω.

Solution
(i) From equation (7.3),

$$I_{d(max)} = 0.4/24 = 16.67 \text{ mA}$$

From equation (7.2),

$$R_s = \frac{30 - 24}{16.67 \times 10^{-3}} = 360 \ \Omega \quad (Ans.)$$

(ii) When the load resistance is 2000 Ω the load current will be $24/2000 = 12$ mA. The total current in R_s is 16.67 mA and

$$\text{Diode current} = 4.67 \text{ mA} \quad (Ans.)$$

(b) Varying supply voltage; Fixed load

If the supply voltage to the stabilizer circuit should decrease, the diode current will fall so that a smaller voltage drop across the series resistor occurs. The Zener diode must pass a minimum current $I_{d(min)}$ if it is to operate in its breakdown region and act as a voltage stabilizer. Therefore

$$R_s = \frac{V_{IN(min)} - V_{OUT}}{I_{d(min)} + I_L} \tag{7.4}$$

Example 7.2

A 9.1 V, 1.3 W Zener diode has a minimum current requirement of 20 mA and is to be used in a stabilizer circuit. The supply voltage is 20 V $\pm$ 10% and the constant load current is 30 mA. Calculate (i) the series resistance required and (ii) the power dissipated in the diode when the supply voltage is 22 V.

Solution
(i) From equation (7.4)

$$R_s = \frac{18 - 9.1}{(20 + 30) \times 10^{-3}} = 178 \ \Omega \quad (Ans.)$$

(ii) When $V_{IN} = 22$ V

$$I_d + I_L = \frac{22 - 9.1}{178} = 72.47 \text{ mA}$$

$$I_d = 72.47 - 30 = 42.47 \text{ mA} \quad (Ans.)$$

and therefore

$$\text{Power dissipated} = 9.1 \times 42.47 \times 10^{-3} = 386 \text{ mW} \quad (Ans.)$$

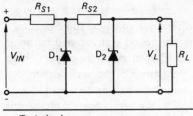

Typical values
$R_{S1} = 330 \, \Omega$, $R_{S2} = 220 \, \Omega$

Fig. 7.16 Double Zener diode stabilizer

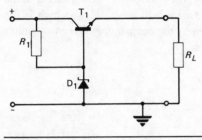

Typical value
$R_1 = 1.2 \, k\Omega$

Fig. 7.17 Emitter-follower stabilizer

(c) Varying supply voltage; Varying load

The maximum value of the series resistor R_s is determined by the necessary minimum diode current, and its minimum value is calculated to be large enough to ensure that the rated power dissipation of the diode is not exceeded. The value chosen for R_s must be a compromise between the minimum and maximum values.

The voltage stability of the basic Zener diode circuit is not good enough for many applications because the internal resistance of the diode is not zero. This means that any change in the current flowing in the diode will cause a small change in the voltage appearing across the diode and hence also in the output voltage. The stability of the output voltage can be improved by cascading two Zener diodes as shown by Fig. 7.16.

The stabilization efficiency of the voltage regulator would be increased if the magnitude of the current flowing in the diode were reduced. The circuit of an emitter-follower voltage stabilizer is shown in Fig. 7.17. Since the transistor is connected as an emitter follower, the voltage at its emitter, which is the load voltage, is very nearly equal to the base voltage. The base voltage is specified by the Zener diode and so the output voltage is held constant within limits determined by the diode characteristics. The emitter-follower stabilizer has no provision for varying the output voltage and its stabilization efficiency is not good enough for many applications.

Series-control Stabilizers

The principle of a much more efficient type of stabilizer is shown in block schematic form by Fig. 7.18.

The output voltage of the rectifier is applied to a series-control element which introduces resistance into the positive supply line. The output voltage V_{OUT} is smaller than the input voltage by the voltage dropped across the series element. The output voltage, or a known fraction of it, is compared in the voltage comparator with a voltage reference. The difference between the two voltages is detected and an amplified version of it is applied to the series-control element in order to vary its resistance in such a way as to maintain the output

Fig. 7.18 Block schematic diagram of series stabilizer

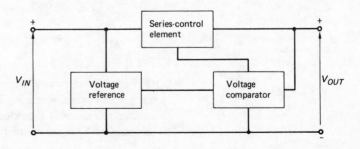

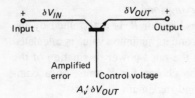

Fig. 7.19 Transistor series-control element

voltage at its correct value. If, for example, the output voltage is larger than it should be, the amplified difference voltage will be of such a polarity that the resistance of the controlled element will be made larger and the output voltage will fall. Conversely, if the output voltage is less than its correct value, the resistance of the series-controlled element will be reduced by the amount necessary for the output voltage to rise to its correct value. Generally, the series-control element is a transistor connected as shown in Fig. 7.19. When an n-p-n transistor is employed, its collector is connected to the input terminal, and its emitter is connected to the output terminal, of the circuit since the former is more positive. If the output voltage of the stabilizer should vary by an amount δV_{OUT}, the control voltage appearing at the base terminal of the series transistor will be $A_v' \delta V_{OUT}$, which is the amplified error voltage produced by the comparator. The base-emitter voltage of the transistor is then

$$A_v' \delta V_{OUT} - \delta V_{OUT}$$

and will produce a voltage

$$A_v'' (A_v' \delta V_{OUT} - \delta V_{OUT})$$

between the base and collector terminals where A_v'' is the voltage gain of the series transistor. The voltage across this transistor is also equal to $\delta V_{IN} - \delta V_{OUT}$ and therefore

$$\delta V_{IN} - \delta V_{OUT} = A_v'' (A_v' \delta V_{OUT} - \delta V_{OUT}) \tag{7.5}$$

Example 7.3

In a voltage stabilizer of the type shown in Fig. 7.18 the error voltage gain of the comparator is –100 and the voltage gain of the series transistor is –10. The rectifier circuit connected to the input terminals of the stabilizer has an output resistance of 200 Ω. Calculate the change in the output voltage that occurs when the load current changes by 20 mA.

Solution

$$\delta V_{IN} = \delta I_L R_{OUT} = 20 \times 10^{-3} \times 200 = 4 \text{ V}$$

Hence, substituting into equation (7.5),

$$4 - \delta V_{OUT} = -10(-100\delta V_{OUT} - \delta V_{OUT})$$

$$4 = 1000\delta V_{OUT} + 10\delta V_{OUT} + \delta V_{OUT}$$

$$\delta V_{OUT} = \frac{4}{1011} = 3.956 \text{ mV} \quad (Ans.)$$

(1) Fig. 7.20 shows the circuit of a voltage stabilizer in which T_1 is the series control element, T_2 is the voltage comparator, and the voltage reference is provided by the Zener diode D_1. The emitter potential of T_2 is maintained at a very nearly constant value by the

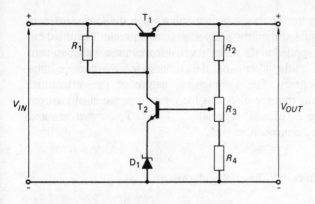

Fig. 7.20 Transistor series stabilizer

Typical values

$R_1 = 3.3$ kΩ, $R_2 = 3.3$ kΩ
$R_3 = 5$ kΩ, $R_4 = 4.7$ kΩ

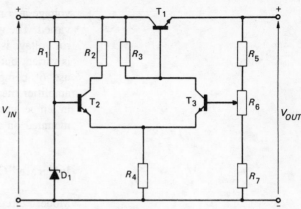

Fig. 7.21 Series stabilizer with differential comparator

Typical values

$R_1 = 4.7$ kΩ, $R_2 = R_3 = 3.3$ kΩ
$R_4 = 1.2$ kΩ, $R_5 = 3.3$ kΩ
$R_6 = 5$ kΩ, $R_7 = 4.7$ kΩ
$D_1 = 5.1$ V

Zener diode D_1, whilst its base is held at a fraction of the output voltage by the potential divider R_2, R_3 and R_4. The difference between the base and emitter potentials is amplified and the amplified error voltage is applied to the base of T_1 to vary the bias voltage provided by resistor R_1. Suppose that the output voltage of the stabilizer should increase above its nominal value (set by variable resistor R_3). The base voltage of T_2 will become more positive, with respect to the constant emitter voltage, and T_2 will conduct a larger collector current. The voltage dropped across R_1 will then increase and this will make the base potential of T_1 less positive. T_1 will now conduct less readily and so its resistance increases. The consequent increase in the collector-emitter voltage of T_1 causes the output voltage to fall by an amount that is very nearly equal to the original increase. The series transistor T_1 must be capable of carrying the full load current of the stabilizer and should have an adequate power rating.

(2) An alternative arrangement that is commonly used is given in Fig. 7.21. The voltage comparator is the *differential* amplifier formed by transistors T_2 and T_3. The differential amplifier, or *long-tailed pair*, produces a change of voltage at the collector of T_3 which is proportional to the difference between the base potentials of T_2 and T_3. The base of T_2 is held at a constant voltage by the potential divider formed by R_1 and D_1, while the base voltage of T_3 is a fraction, determined by R_5, R_6 and R_7, of the output voltage. The circuit acts in a similar manner to the previous stabilizer to maintain the output

voltage at a more, or less, constant value when the load current is varied. The voltage stability is superior since a greater amplified error voltage is applied to the series transistor when the output voltage is varied, but, on the other hand, the circuit is more expensive in its use of components. The symmetrical nature of the differential amplifier means that the effect on the circuit operation of changes in temperature is reduced, especially if T_2 and T_3 are matched and mounted on a common heat sink.

Integrated Circuit Voltage Regulators

Modern circuitry generally employs an IC voltage regulator to provide the required power supply voltage stability. Devices are available of varying degrees of complexity that are capable of satisfying all but the most stringent of specifications. The simplest voltage regulators, which are perfectly adequate for many applications, are **three-terminal** types. Representative of 3-terminal regulators are devices in the 7800 series.

The 7800 series of voltage regulators are able to provide an output current of up to 1.5 A with one of a number of fixed output voltages. If an excess current, or overheating, should occur the IC will shut down to prevent any damage being caused. The output voltage of a 7800 regulator is indicated by the last two figures in the device number. Thus, the 7805 provides an output voltage of 5 V, the 7808 provides 8 V, the 7812 provides 12 V and so on. The manufacturer's data sheet for the 7805 includes:

Data Sheet for the 7805

d.c. input voltage for	V_{OUT} = 5 to 18 V	35 V max.
for	V_{OUT} = 24 V	40 V max.
Quiescent current typ.	4.2 mA, max. 6 mA	
Output voltage min.	4.8 V, typ. 5 V, max. 5.2 V	
Temperature coefficient at	I_{OUT} = 5 mA –1.1 mV/°C	
Line regulation $\dfrac{\delta V_{IN}}{\delta V_{OUT}}$	(V_{IN} = 8 V → 12 V) 1 mV typ. 25 mV max.	
Load regulation $\dfrac{\delta V_{OUT}}{V_{OUT}}$	15 mV typ. 50 mV max.	
Output resistance	17 mΩ	

The IC can be used to produce a fixed output voltage in the way shown by Fig. 7.22. Capacitor C_2 is usually fitted to keep the output resistance of the circuit low at high frequencies. If the regulator is not sited immediately after the rectifier circuit itself an input capacitor C_1 is also necessary.

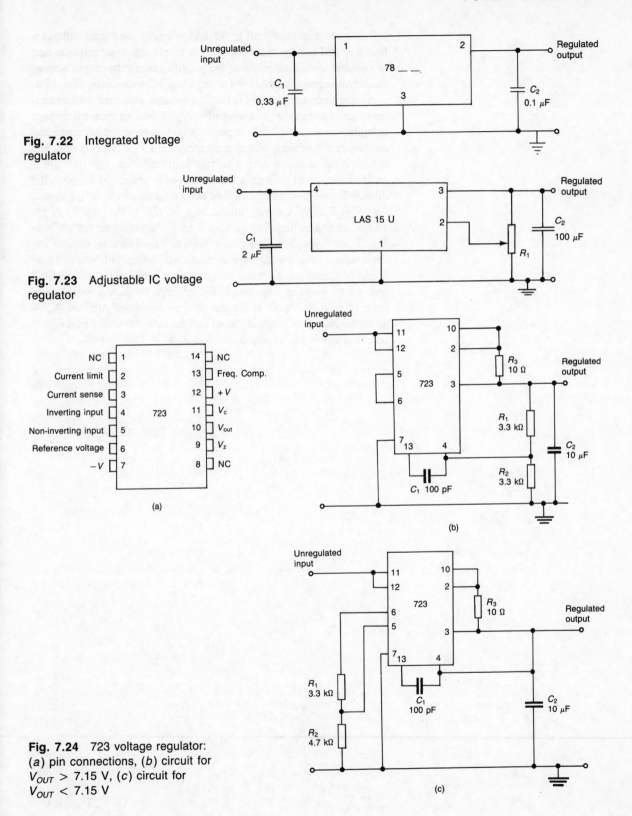

Fig. 7.22 Integrated voltage regulator

Fig. 7.23 Adjustable IC voltage regulator

Fig. 7.24 723 voltage regulator: (*a*) pin connections, (*b*) circuit for $V_{OUT} > 7.15$ V, (*c*) circuit for $V_{OUT} < 7.15$ V

If there is a requirement to be able to adjust the output voltage a four-terminal voltage regulator must be employed. The fourth pin acts as a control terminal that allows the output voltage to be set to a wanted value. An example of this kind of regulator IC is shown by Fig. 7.23.

A commonly used circuit is the 723 voltage regulator; the pin connections of the device are given by Fig. 7.24. An internal voltage reference provides 7.15 V at pin 6. This voltage must be connected either directly or via a potential divider to pin 5. A direct connection is used if the required output voltage is greater than 7.15 V, adjustment of the output voltage is then achieved by means of the potential divider $R_1 + R_2$ connected across the output terminals of the circuit (see Fig. 7.24b). Output voltage $V_{OUT} = (R_1 + R_2)7.15/R_2$. If the wanted output voltage is less than 7.15 V the arrangement given in Fig. 7.24c is employed, it can be seen that the potential divider has been moved from the output terminals to the connection between pins 5 and 6. Capacitor C_1 must be connected between the terminals 4 and 13 to prevent any possibility of high-frequency oscillations occurring. Resistor R_3 is chosen to give a voltage drop of 0.5 V when the maximum wanted output current flows; then any excess current will cause the regulator to shut down.

8 Digital Circuits

Modern electronics make ever increasing use of **digital electronic** circuitry which responds only to signals that can only take up either one of two **logic levels**. Either the signal is HIGH, usually between about 2.5 V to 5 V, or it is LOW, usually between about 0 V to 0.4 V. Information is transmitted in the form of a number of voltage pulses that vary between the two values, Fig. 8.1 showing two examples. For a pulse waveform to carry information or *data* some kind of *code* must be used. The basic code employed is the binary code but various extensions of this are often employed, such as the ASCII code and binary coded decimal.

A simple example of a digital signalling system is shown in Fig. 8.2. An earthed battery and a key are connected to one end of a telephone line and an earthed lamp is connected to the other end. When the key is unoperated the circuit is broken and no current flows into the line; the lamp is not lit. When the key is pressed, the circuit is completed and the current flowing through the lamp causes it to light. The lamp and the switch are examples of *two-state devices*. For information to be transmitted over the line the key must be operated in accordance with some code.

The Binary Code

In digital electronic systems, the devices have two stable states, ON and OFF, and for this reason the binary number system is used. In the binary system only two digits 0 and 1 exist. Larger numbers are obtained by utilizing the powers of two. The digit at the right-hand side of a binary number represents a multiple (0 or 1) of 2^0; the next digit to the left represents a multiple of 2^1; and so on as shown by Table 8.1. The binary digits are generally known as **bits**.

The value of each power of two is given in the table and any desired number can be attained by a correct choice of zeros and ones. Thus, number 18 for example: 18 is equal to 16 plus 2 and is therefore given by 0010010 in a 7-bit code or by 10010 if only 5 bits are used. Reading from the right (the *least significant bit* or *lsb*), the number consists of zero 1, one 2, zero 4, zero 8 and one 16. Similarly, the binary

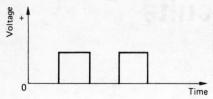

Fig. 8.1 Digital waveforms

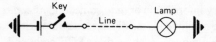

Fig. 8.2 Simple digital circuit

Table 8.1

2^8	2^7	2^6	2^5	2^4	2^3	2^2	2^1	2^0
256	128	64	32	16	8	4	2	1

Table 8.2

7	00000111	25	00011001	80	01010000
17	00010001	31	00011111	150	10010110

equivalents of some other numbers are given in Table 8.2, assuming an 8-bit code.

Some typical examples of digital systems are the following: (*a*) the digital computer, and communication with a computer over telephone lines; (*b*) the control of traffic lights, of lifts in tall buildings, of conveyor belts in factories, etc.; (*c*) safety arrangements for cranes and various factory machines; (*d*) electronic counting systems such as counting the number of cars in a car park; (*e*) digital voltmeters; (*f*) digital watches; and (*g*) pocket calculators.

Two-state Devices

A two-state device is one which has only two stable operating conditions, or states. Two examples of two-state devices have already been introduced in this chapter, namely the lamp, and the switch. In both of these cases the device is either operated or it is not, i.e. either it is ON or it is OFF. The two binary conditions 1 and 0 can therefore be represented by a two-state device. Either of two conventions can be adopted; logical 1 can be represented by the ON condition and logical 0 by the OFF state, or alternatively, the ON state can mean logical 0 and the OFF state logical 1. Other examples of two-state devices are the semiconductor diode and the junction or field-effect transistor. When turned ON, or fully conducting, a transistor represents the binary 0 logic state and when turned OFF, or non-conducting, it represents the binary 1 logic state.

Combinational Logic Gates

An electronic gate is a logic element which is able to operate on an applied binary signal in a manner determined by its logical function. A number of different types of gate feature in digital circuitry, the most common of which are (i) the AND gate, (ii) the OR gate, (iii) the NOT gate, (iv) the NOR gate, and (v) the NAND gate.

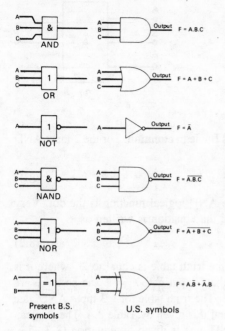

Fig. 8.3 Gate symbols

The British Standards Institution (BSI) symbol for an AND gate is given in Fig. 8.3. The & sign can be replaced by a number indicating the number of inputs which must go high to make the output go high. The American gate symbols are also shown in Fig. 8.3.

Modern logic circuitry is invariably produced using **integrated circuit technology**.

The majority of digital ICs belong to either the **cmos** or the **ttl** logic families. The latter family has several sub-groups of which the most popular is known as low-power Schottky ttl. The use of ICs for electronic equipment results in greater reliability and lower costs and allows complex circuit functions to be economically produced. Because of this, complex circuitry such as is used in quartz watches, pocket calculators and home computers has become relatively inexpensive and is commonly employed.

In both the cmos and the ttl families, a standard package may accommodate more than one gate. For example, readily available are

    (i) Quad 2-input NAND or NOR gates
   (ii) Triple 3-input NAND or NOR gates
  (iii) Dual 4-input NAND or NOR gates
  (iv) Single 8-input NAND or NOR gates.

The NOT Gate

The NOT gate, or inverter, is used to invert a logic term, e.g. change logical 0 into logical 1 or 1 to 0. The symbol for a NOT gate is shown in Fig. 8.3. In a Boolean expression the NOT logical function is indicated by a bar placed over a symbol. Thus $\bar{A}$ means 'NOT A'.

The NOT function is provided in both the cmos and the ttl logic families by a **hex inverter**. This IC, for example the ttl 7404, consists of six independent inverters or NOT gates in the one IC package.

The AND Gate

The AND gate is a logic circuit having two, or more, input terminals, labelled A,B,C, etc., and a single output terminal, usually labelled F. The output F of an AND gate is HIGH, or at logical 1, only if ALL of its inputs are HIGH, or at logical 1. If any one, or more, of the inputs are LOW, or at logical 0, then the output of the circuit will be LOW, or at logical 0.

The symbols for 2-input and 3-input AND gates are shown in Fig. 8.4. The logical operation of a gate can be described by a **truth table**. The truth table of a logic circuit shows the logical state of the output of the circuit for all the possible combinations of the logical states of the inputs to the circuit. Table 8.3 gives the truth table for the 2-input AND gate. The logical operation of a gate can also be

Table 8.3

A	0	1	0	1
B	0	0	1	1
F	0	0	0	1

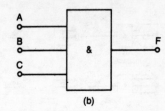

Fig. 8.4 2-input, and 3-input AND gates

described by writing down its **Boolean equation**. For the 2-input AND gate this is

$$F = A.B \tag{8.1}$$

The Boolean symbol for the AND logical function is the dot. Very often the dot is omitted and the equation is written as

$$F = AB \tag{8.2}$$

The number of columns in a truth table is equal to 2^n, where n is the number of inputs. For the 2-input gate $n = 2$ and so there are 2^2 or 4 columns in Table 8.3. The truth table for a 3-input AND gate must have 2^3 or 8 columns and it is given by Table 8.4. The Boolean equation for the 3-input AND gate is given by equation (8.3), i.e.

$$F = ABC \tag{8.3}$$

Table 8.4

A	0	1	0	1	0	1	0	1
B	0	0	1	1	0	0	1	1
C	0	0	0	0	1	1	1	1
F	0	0	0	0	0	0	0	1

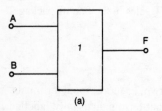

(a)

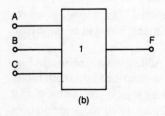

(b)

Fig. 8.5 2-input, and 3-input OR gates

The OR Gate

The OR gate, Fig. 8.5, has its output F at the logical 1 level whenever any one, or more, of its inputs are at logical 1. The output of the gate will be at logical 0 only if all of its inputs are at logical 0. Table 8.5 gives the truth tables for 2-input and 3-input OR gates. The Boolean equations for each gate are given by equations (8.4) and (8.5) respectively, i.e.

$$F = A + B \tag{8.4}$$

$$F = A + B + C \tag{8.5}$$

Note that the symbol for the OR logical function is the + sign.

Table 8.5

A	0	1	0	1	A	0	1	0	1	0	1	0	1
B	0	0	1	1	B	0	0	1	1	0	0	1	1
F	0	1	1	1	C	0	0	0	0	1	1	1	1
					F	0	1	1	1	1	1	1	1

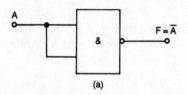

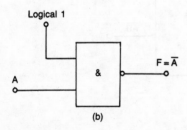

Fig. 8.6 NAND gate

Fig. 8.7 NAND gate connected as an inverter

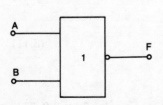

Fig. 8.8 NOR gate

The NAND Gate

The NAND gate, Fig. 8.6, performs the inverse logical function to the AND gate. The output of a NAND gate is at 0 only if all of the inputs to the gate are at 1. The truth table of 2-input and 3-input NAND gates are given by Table 8.6. The Boolean expressions for the two NAND gates are given by equations (8.6) and (8.7) respectively.

$$F = \overline{AB} \tag{8.6}$$

$$F = \overline{ABC} \tag{8.7}$$

The NOT function can be produced using a NAND gate in two different ways. Referring to the truth table of the 2-input NAND gate it can be seen that:

(a) if the inputs A and B are connected together so that $A = B$, Fig. 8.7a, the output will always be inverted, and

(b) if either input is held at the logical 1 voltage level, Fig. 8.7b, the output will always be NOT the logical state of the other input.

Table 8.6

A	0	1	0	1	A	0	1	0	1	0	1	0	1
B	0	0	1	1	B	0	0	1	1	0	0	1	1
F	1	1	1	0	C	0	0	0	0	1	1	1	1
					F	1	1	1	1	1	1	1	0

The NOR Gate

The NOR gate, Fig. 8.8, performs the inverse of the logical OR function. This means that the output F of a NOR gate is at logical 1 only when all of its inputs are at logical 0. The truth tables for both 2-input and 3-input NOR gates are given by Table 8.7. The Boolean expressions for the two gates are given by equations (8.8) and (8.9), i.e.

$$F = \overline{A + B} \tag{8.8}$$

$$F = \overline{A + B + C} \tag{8.9}$$

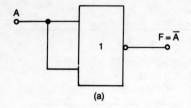

(a)

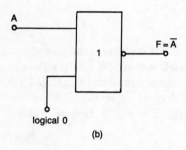

logical 0

(b)

Fig. 8.9 NOR gate connected as an inverter

Table 8.7

A	0	1	0	1	A	0	1	0	1	0	1	0	1
B	0	0	1	1	B	0	0	1	1	0	0	1	1
F	1	0	0	0	C	0	0	0	0	1	1	1	1
					F	1	0	0	0	0	0	0	0

The NOT function can be generated by a NOR gate if either (a) both its input terminals are connected together, Fig. 8.9a, or (b) one input is connected to the logical 0 voltage level, Fig. 8.9b.

Combinations of Gates

Very often it is convenient to be able to perform a logical function using a different kind of gate.

AND Followed by NOT

If an AND gate is followed by a NOT gate (see Fig. 8.10) the output of the circuit will be $\overline{AB}$. Therefore, the combination acts like a NAND gate.

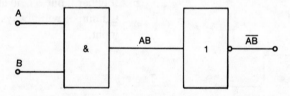

Fig. 8.10 Performs the NAND logical function

AND Preceded by NOT

If all of the inputs to an AND gate are inverted, see Fig. 8.11, the output of the circuit will be $F = \bar{A}.\bar{B}$. The truth table for this equation is given by Table 8.8. If this table is compared with the truth tables of the various gates it will be seen that the NOR logical function has been performed. Therefore,

$$F = \bar{A}\bar{B} = \overline{A + B} \tag{8.10}$$

Similarly,

$$F = \bar{A}\bar{B}\bar{C} = \overline{A + B + C} \tag{8.11}$$

NAND Preceded by NOT

The truth table for the circuit of Fig. 8.12 is given by Table 8.9. This shows that the output of the circuit is 1 whenever any one, or more,

Table 8.8

A	0	1	0	1
B	0	0	1	1
Ā	1	0	1	0
B̄	1	1	0	0
F = ĀB̄	1	0	0	0

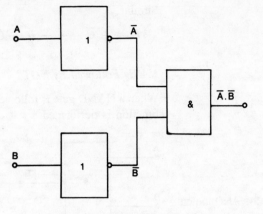

Fig. 8.11 Performs the NOR logical function

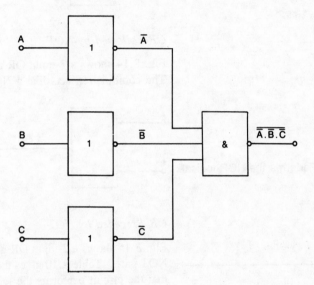

Fig. 8.12 Performs the OR logical function

Table 8.9

A	0	1	0	1	0	1	0	1
B	0	0	1	1	0	0	1	1
C	0	0	0	0	1	1	1	1
$\bar{A}$	1	0	1	0	1	0	1	0
$\bar{B}$	1	1	0	0	1	1	0	0
$\bar{C}$	1	1	1	1	0	0	0	0
$F = \overline{\bar{A}\bar{B}\bar{C}}$	0	1	1	1	1	1	1	1

of its inputs is at 1. This means that the circuit performs the OR logical function. The Boolean expression for the circuit is

$$F = \overline{\bar{A}\bar{B}\bar{C}} = A + B + C \tag{8.12}$$

Similarly,

$$F = \overline{\overline{A}\overline{B}\overline{C}} = \overline{A} + \overline{B} + \overline{C} \qquad (8.13)$$

NAND Followed by NOT

When a NAND gate is followed by a NOT gate, Fig. 8.13, the AND function is performed.

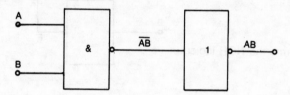

Fig. 8.13 Performs the AND logical function

OR Followed by NOT

Fig. 8.14 shows a 2-input OR gate that is followed by a NOT gate. The combination acts like a NOR gate.

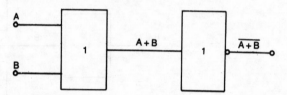

Fig. 8.14 Performs the NOR logical function

OR Preceded by NOT

Table 8.10

A	0	1	0	1
B	0	0	1	1
$\overline{A}$	1	0	1	0
$\overline{B}$	1	1	0	0
$F = \overline{A} + \overline{B}$	1	1	1	0

Fig. 8.15 shows a 2-input OR gate that has both of its inputs fed via NOT gates. Table 8.10 gives the truth table of the circuit and shows that the circuit performs the logical function NAND. The Boolean expression describing the circuit is given by equation (8.14), i.e.

$$F = \overline{A} + \overline{B} = \overline{AB} \qquad (8.14)$$

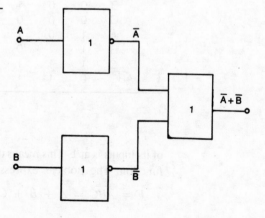

Fig. 8.15 Performs the NAND logical function

NOR Followed by NOT

Fig. 8.16 shows a NOR gate followed by an inverter. The OR logical function is performed.

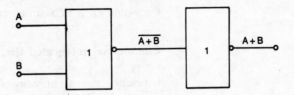

Fig. 8.16 Performs the OR logical function

NOR Preceded by NOT

Fig. 8.17 shows a NOR gate both of whose inputs are passed through a NOT gate. The truth table of the arrangement is given by Table 8.11. The output of the circuit is at logical 1 only when both of its inputs are at logical 1. Hence, the circuit performs the AND logical function. The Boolean expression for the circuit is given by equation (8.15), i.e.

$$F = \overline{\bar{A} + \bar{B}} = AB \tag{8.15}$$

Table 8.11

A	0	1	0	1
B	0	0	1	1
$\bar{A}$	1	0	1	0
$\bar{B}$	1	1	0	0
$F = \overline{\bar{A} + \bar{B}}$	0	0	0	1

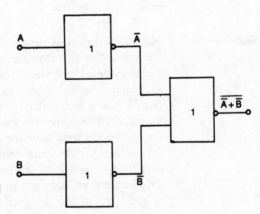

Fig. 8.17 Performs the AND logical function

De Morgan's Rules

The two rules attributed to De Morgan are

$$\textbf{A} \quad \overline{AB} = \bar{A} + \bar{B} \tag{8.16}$$

$$\textbf{B} \quad \overline{A + B} = \bar{A}\bar{B} \tag{8.17}$$

Both of these rules have already been arrived at by the use of truth tables, see Tables 8.9 and 8.11. The rules governing the application of De Morgan's theorems are:

(*a*) invert the variables,

(b) change the connections,

(c) invert the whole expression.

Since either of De Morgan's rules produces the equivalent of any expression to which it is applied it can be applied to any part of, or the whole of, a Boolean expression.

Commercial Integrated Circuits

In practice, the vast majority of the gates employed in digital circuitry are members of either the ttl or the cmos logic families. Some ttl examples, showing IC package pin connections are given in Fig. 8.18a. The ttl family includes the standard 74 series, the low-power Schottky 74LS series, the advanced Schottky 74AS series, and the advanced low-power Schottky 74ALS series. The examples given in Fig. 8.18a (p. 132) have representatives in each series.

The cmos logic family includes the standard 4000 series and the high-speed hcmos series. Some examples of the 4000 series gates are given by Fig. 8.18b (p. 133).

It is normally preferable for economic reasons for one circuit to employ ICs from only one logic family. The choice is based upon a number of factors, such as power dissipation and speed of operation.

Combinational Logic Circuits

Many digital circuits consist of a number of gates which have been interconnected to perform a wanted logical function. The design of a combinational logic circuit starts with the truth table which describes the required logical operation. Once the truth table has been written down it can be used to derive the Boolean expression which describes the circuit. The expression should contain one term for each column (or row) in the truth table for which the output F of the circuit is at the logical 1 state. The expression so obtained should then be simplified, or *minimized*, if possible to eliminate all unnecessary terms. This step ensures that the final circuit contains the minimum number of gates. Next, the designed circuit is usually converted into an equivalent circuit that uses *either* NAND *or* NOR gates only. Besides very often reducing the number of integrated circuits required the use of just one kind of gate makes both manufacture and fault-finding somewhat easier.

The minimization of a Boolean expression can be carried out using either algebraic or mapping methods. The algebraic method is based upon a number of rules, some of which are quoted in Table 8.12. It is more convenient, and easier, however to use a **Karnaugh map**.

Table 8.12

$A + 1 = 1$	$A.1 = A$	$A + A = A$	$A.A = A$
$A.\bar{A} = 0$	$A + \bar{A} = 1$	$A.0 = 0$	$A + 0 = A$

The Karnaugh Map

The Karnaugh map is a graphical representation of *all* the combinations of the input variables that can exist in a logical circuit. The map consists of a number of squares, each of which represents a unique combination of the input variables. This means that the number of squares in a map must be equal to 2^n, where *n* is the number of input variables.

This means that a Boolean expression with two variables must be represented by a 4-square map, and an expression with three variables by an 8-square map, as shown.

	A	$\bar{A}$
B	AB	$\bar{A}$B
$\bar{B}$	A$\bar{B}$	$\bar{A}\bar{B}$

	A		$\bar{A}$	
C	ABC	A$\bar{B}$C	$\bar{A}\bar{B}$C	$\bar{A}$BC
$\bar{C}$	AB$\bar{C}$	A$\bar{B}\bar{C}$	$\bar{A}\bar{B}\bar{C}$	$\bar{A}$B$\bar{C}$
	B	$\bar{B}$		B

To map an equation the equation should first be put into the **sum-of-products** form, e.g. F $=$ ABC $+$ $\bar{A}$B$\bar{C}$ $+$ A$\bar{B}\bar{C}$. Each term in the equation is mapped by a 1 in the appropriate square. Each term that is not present in the equation is mapped by a 0 in the appropriate square. Thus for the expression quoted previously the mapping is:

	A		$\bar{A}$	
C	1	0	0	0
$\bar{C}$	0	1	0	1
	B	$\bar{B}$		B

A term like *AB* is mapped by putting a 1 into two squares. The term can be rewritten as $AB(C+\bar{C})$ (since $C+\bar{C} = 1$) or $ABC + AB\bar{C}$ and so the mapping is:

	A		$\bar{A}$	
C	1	0	0	0
$\bar{C}$	1	0	0	0
	B	$\bar{B}$		B

A single variable, such as *B* for example, is mapped by putting 1 into four squares; *B* can be rewritten as $B(A+\bar{A})$ $(C+\bar{C}) = ABC + AB\bar{C} + \bar{A}BC + \bar{A}B\bar{C}$ and so the mapping is:

	A		$\bar{A}$	
C	1	0	0	1
$\bar{C}$	1	0	0	1
	B	$\bar{B}$		B

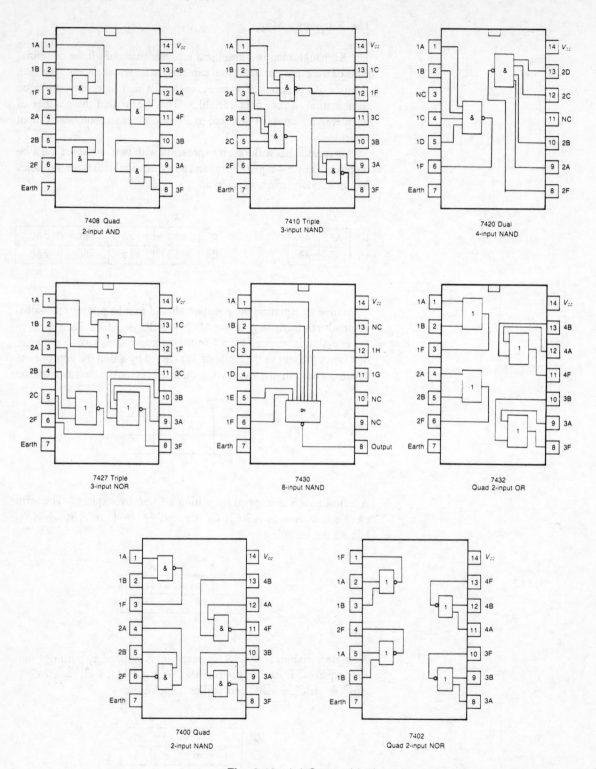

Fig. 8.18 (*a*) Some ttl logic gates, (*b*) some cmos logic gates

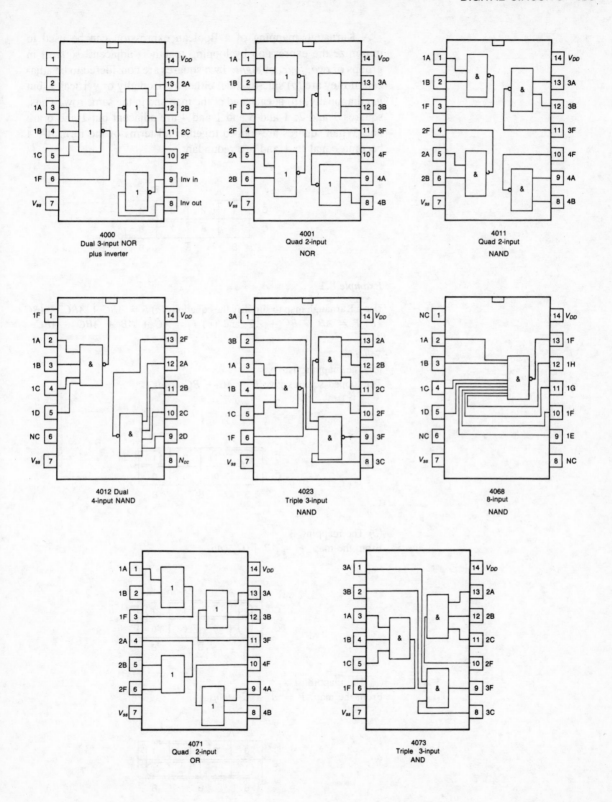

4000
Dual 3-input NOR
plus inverter

4001
Quad 2-input
NOR

4011
Quad 2-input
NAND

4012 Dual
4-input NAND

4023
Triple 3-input
NAND

4068
8-input
NAND

4071
Quad 2-input
OR

4073
Triple 3-input
AND

A Karnaugh mapping of a Boolean expression can be used to minimize the expression by looping together 'adjacent' squares in groups of *two, four*, or *eight*. Two squares are considered to be adjacent if they are (*a*) side-by-side, either horizontally or vertically, but *not* diagonally, (*b*) at each end of the map and in the same row. Thus, squares 1 and 2, 1 and 5 and 1 and 4 are adjacent but 1 and 6 are not. When squares are looped together all terms of the form $A + \bar{A}$ become equal to 1 and are redundant.

	A		$\bar{A}$	
C	1	2	3	4
$\bar{C}$	5	6	7	8
	B	$\bar{B}$		B

Example 8.1

Use a Karnaugh map to simplify the equations (*a*) $F = ABC + A\bar{B}C + \bar{A}BC$ (*b*) $F = AB + \bar{B}C + \bar{A}C$, and (*c*) $F = A\bar{C} + \bar{A}B + \bar{A}BC + \bar{A}\bar{B}\bar{C}$.

Solution
(*a*) The mapping is:
The looped squares give $F = AC + BC$ (*Ans.*)

	A		$\bar{A}$	
C	1	1	0	1
$\bar{C}$	0	0	0	0
	B	$\bar{B}$		B

(*b*) The mapping is:
From the map, $F = AB + C$ (*Ans.*)

	A		$\bar{A}$	
C	1	1	1	1
$\bar{C}$	1	0	0	0
	B	$\bar{B}$		B

(*c*) The mapping is:
From the map, $F = \bar{A} + \bar{C}$ (*Ans.*)

	A		$\bar{A}$	
C	0	0	1	1
$\bar{C}$	1	1	1	1
	B	$\bar{B}$		B

Table 8.13

A	0	1	0	1	0	1	0	1
B	0	0	1	1	0	0	1	1
C	0	0	0	0	1	1	1	1
F	0	1	0	1	1	1	0	1

Design Example

Table 8.13 gives the truth table of a combinational logic circuit that is to be designed.

The Boolean expression describing the logical operation of the circuit is $F = A\bar{B}\bar{C} + AB\bar{C} + A\bar{B}C + \bar{A}\bar{B}C + ABC$. This expression should be mapped to see whether any simplification is possible. The mapping is:

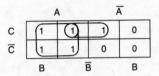

From the map, $F = A + \bar{B}C$. Once the minimal Boolean expression has been obtained it must be implemented using the appropriate gates. Three possibilities exist. The wanted circuit can be implemented

- (a) using AND, OR and NOT gates,
- (b) using NAND gate only, or
- (c) using NOR gate only.

In both the ttl and the cmos logic families NAND and NOR gates are cheaper, faster to operate, and dissipate less power than AND or OR gates. It is also advantageous from both the manufacturing and maintenance points of view if a circuit uses just one type of gate throughout. It is therefore common practice to construct a circuit using either NAND or NOR gates alone.

The next step in deriving the wanted circuit should be to draw the logic diagram using AND, OR and NOT gates. The diagram can then be converted to one using either NAND or NOR gates only by simply replacing each AND/OR/NOT gate by its NAND/NOR equivalent.

The final steps are then to decide which integrated circuits will be used to construct the final circuit.

Suppose the expression to be implemented is $F = A + \bar{B}C$.

- (a) The logic diagram using AND/OR/NOT gates is shown in Fig. 8.19. One AND, one OR and one NOT gate are needed, necessitating the use of three integrated circuits.
- (b) The NAND equivalent of Fig. 8.19 is obtained by replacing each gate by its NAND gate equivalent (refer to Figs. 8.7, 8.12 and 8.13). The circuit obtained is shown in Fig. 8.20a. It might seem, at first sight, that six gates are now needed but two of these gates give successive inversions and are therefore redundant. Removing the redundant gates gives the final circuit of Fig. 8.20b. This circuit contains four NAND gates and

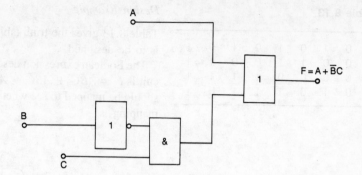

Fig. 8.19

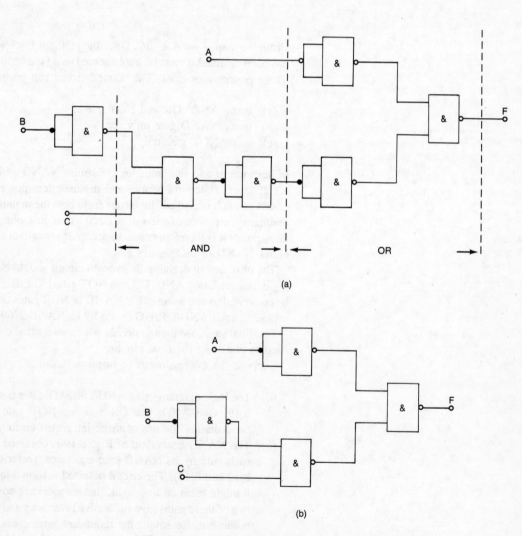

(a)

(b)

Fig. 8.20 NAND gate implementation of Fig. 8.19

will only need one integrated circuit. Fig. 8.21 shows the circuit constructed with a 7400 quad 2-input NAND gate.

(c) The NOR gate version of Fig. 8.19 can similarly be obtained. Fig. 8.22a shows the first logic circuit diagram and Fig. 8.22b shows the final circuit after redundant gates have been removed. Again, four gates are needed and the circuit could be fabricated using the 7402 quad 2-input NOR gate.

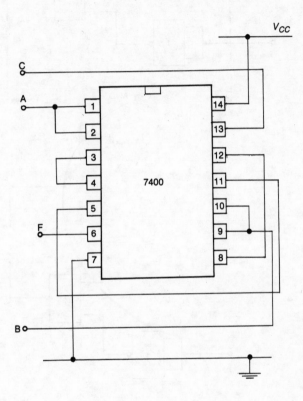

Fig. 8.21 Fig. 8.20 implemented using a 7400

Sequential Logic Circuits

A sequential logic circuit is one that is able to store one bit, or more, of data and whose output depends upon both stored data and new input data.

The basic sequential logic circuit is the **flip-flop**. A flip-flop is a circuit which has two stable states, either it is SET, i.e. its Q output is at logical 1, or it is RESET, i.e. its Q output is at logical 0. There are four kinds of flip-flop in use; these are known as the $S-R$, the $J-K$, the D, and the T flip-flops. A flip-flop may be used on its own in a circuit, when it is used as a 1-bit store, or it may be used in conjunction with one, or more, other flip-flops to form a **counter** or a **shift register**.

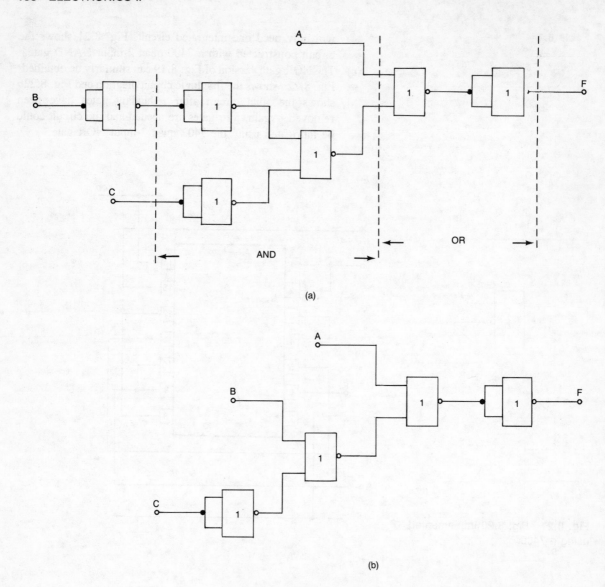

(a)

(b)

Fig. 8.22 NOR gate implementation of Fig. 8.19

Flip-Flops

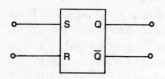

Fig. 8.23 S-R flip-flop

The $S-R$ Flip-Flop

The $S-R$ flip-flop is a circuit that has two input terminals S and R, and two output terminals Q and $\bar{Q}$. In addition, an $S-R$ flip-flop may be **clocked**; this means that a rectangular pulse waveform, known as the **clock**, is applied to a third input terminal to determine the times at which the circuit changes state. The symbol for an $S-R$ flip-flop is shown by Fig. 8.23.

The truth table of an $S-R$ flip-flop is given by Table 8.14. In this, Q is the present state of the Q output terminal and Q^+ is the next

Table 8.14

S	R	Q	Q⁺	
0	0	0	0	No change
0	0	1	1	
1	0	0	1	Set
1	0	1	1	
0	1	0	0	Reset
0	1	1	0	
1	1	0	X	Indeterminate
1	1	1	X	

state. At all times the $\bar{Q}$ terminal is complementary to the Q terminal, i.e. if $Q = 1$ then $\bar{Q} = 0$.

(a) When both the S and R input terminals are at the logical 0 level the flip-flop will remain in its present state, i.e. $Q^+ = Q$.

(b) When $S = 1$ and $R = 0$ the next state of the circuit will be $Q = 1$, $\bar{Q} = 0$, whatever the present state. The flip-flop is said to be SET.

(c) When $S = 0$ and $R = 1$, the next state of the circuit will be $Q = 0$, $\bar{Q} = 1$, whatever the present state. The circuit is said to be RESET.

(d) When both the S and the R inputs are at 1 the flip-flop may, or may not, change states. The next state is *not* predictable and is said to be *indeterminate*. Such a condition cannot be tolerated in a practical system and if there is a possibility of the state $S = R = 1$ arising then the $S{-}R$ flip-flop should not be used.

The $S{-}R$ flip-flop can be obtained as an integrated circuit, e.g. ttl 7471 and cmos 4043, but it can also be made using either NAND or NOR gates. Fig. 8.24 shows how two NOR gates can be interconnected to produce an $S{-}R$ flip-flop.

If two NAND gates are similarly connected, as in Fig. 8.25a, the truth table has the 'no-change' and 'indeterminate' states interchanged. To obtain the true $S{-}R$ flip-flop logical operation two further NAND gates are needed, connected as shown by Fig. 8.25b.

Often it is desirable that the switching of the flip-flop occurs at definite instants in time that are specified by the clock. The NAND $S{-}R$ flip-flop is easily modified to give clocked operation (see Fig. 8.26). Whenever the clock is at logical 0 the outputs of both of the input NAND gates must be at 1 regardless of the logical states of the

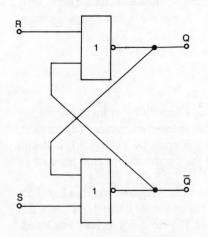

Fig. 8.24 NOR gate S-R flip-flop

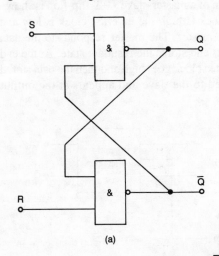

(a)

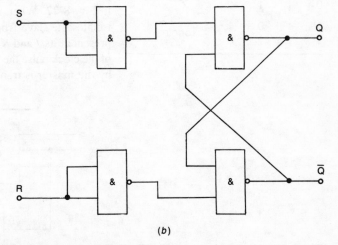

(b)

Fig. 8.25 NAND gate *S-R* flip-flop

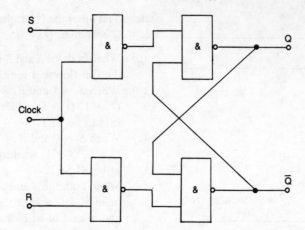

Fig. 8.26 Clocked NAND gate *S-R* flip-flop

S and R inputs. The circuit will then be unable to change state. Only when the clock input is at logical 1 will the S and R inputs control the operation of the circuit.

The J–K Flip-Flop

Table 8.15

J	K	Q	Q⁺	
0	0	0	0	No change
0	0	1	1	
1	0	0	1	Set
1	0	1	1	
0	1	0	0	Reset
0	1	1	0	
1	1	0	1	Toggles
1	1	1	0	

The $J–K$ flip-flop has a truth table which differs from that of the $S–R$ flip-flop only in that the unwanted indeterminate state does not exist. The truth table of a $J–K$ flip-flop is given by Table 8.15. It should be noted that when $S = R = 1$ the circuit *always* changes state or **toggles**.

A $J–K$ flip-flop can be made by modifying the circuit of Fig. 8.26 but the resulting circuit is subject to unwanted **hazards**. Instead, one of the many integrated circuit $J–K$ flip-flops is generally employed. Integrated $J–K$ flip-flops are either **master-slave** or **edge-triggered** devices. The block diagram of a master-slave $J–K$ flip-flop is shown in Fig. 8.27. When the clock is high the inverted clock is low and isolates the slave from the master. The master responds to the data present at its J and K inputs and stores the resultant state. At the end of the clock pulse the inverted clock goes high and then the data stored by the master is transferred to the slave and appears at the output

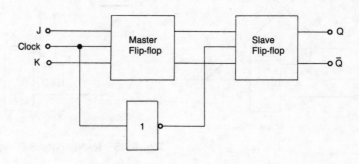

Fig. 8.27 Master-slave J-K flip-flop

terminals. This means that the output state of a master-slave $J-K$ flip-flop changes at the trailing edge of the clock pulse.

Most IC $J-K$ flip-flops are edge-triggered. This means that they change state, as determined by the J and K inputs, *either* as the clock changes from 1 to 0 — a trailing-edge-triggered device — *or* as the clock changes from 0 to 1 — a leading-edge-triggered device. Leading-edge triggering is indicated by a wedge on the clock input of the flip-flop symbol, Fig. 8.28a. Trailing-edge triggering is indicated by the addition of a small circle, Fig. 8.28b.

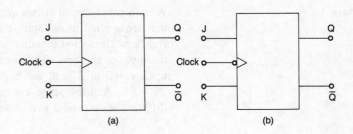

Fig. 8.28 Edge-triggered J-K flip-flops: (a) leading edge, (b) trailing edge

Table 8.16

D	Q	Q⁺
0	0	0
0	1	0
1	0	1
1	1	1

Note: Q⁺ represents Q^+

The D Flip-Flop

The D flip-flop has one input terminal, a clock terminal, and two output terminals, see Fig. 8.29a. The truth table of a D flip-flop is given by Table 8.16. Clearly, the Q output always takes up the logical state of the D input. The D flip-flop is readily available in both the ttl and the cmos logic families but it can also be obtained by modifying a $J-K$ (or $S-R$) flip-flop in the manner shown by Fig. 8.29b.

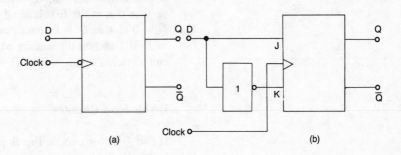

Fig. 8.29 D flip-flop

Table 8.17

T	Q	Q⁺
0	0	0
0	1	1
1	0	1
1	1	0

The T Flip-Flop

The truth table of a T flip-flop is given by Table 8.17. It can be seen that every time there is a pulse at the T input the circuit toggles. The T flip-flop is not available as a separate integrated circuit: when one is wanted it is easily made by merely connecting together the J and K inputs of a $J-K$ flip-flop (Fig. 8.30).

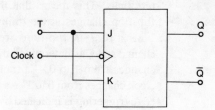

Fig. 8.30 *T* flip-flop

Counters

A counter is a digital circuit that is able to count the number of pulses that are applied to its input terminals. It consists of a number n of flip-flops connected together so that the output of one is applied to the input of the next. The number of states that a counter can take up is equal to 2^n and the highest number which can be stored is $2^n - 1$. A three stage counter, for example, can have 2^3 or 8 different states and a maximum count of 7.

Divide-by 2 Counter

Two ways of obtaining a divide-by-two counter are shown by Figs. 8.31a and b. The $J-K$ flip-flop has both its J and K inputs held permanently at logical 1. The circuit toggles at the end of each clock pulse and generates an output pulse waveform at one-half the clock frequency. The circuit waveforms are given in Fig. 8.31c. The D flip-flop can be converted to operate as a divide-by-2 counter by connecting its D and $\bar{Q}$ terminals together as shown in Fig. 8.31b. The circuit's input and output waveforms are given in Fig. 8.31d. It can be seen that at the first leading edge of the clock, when $Q = 1$ and $\bar{Q} = 0$ so that $D = 0$, the circuit switches to have $Q = 0$. Now $\bar{Q} = D = 1$ and on the leading edge of the second clock pulse the circuit switches again so that $Q = 1$, $\bar{Q} = 0$ and so on.

Divide-by-4 Counter

If two $J-K$, or two D, flip-flops are cascaded, Fig. 8.32, a divide-by-4 counter will be produced. Consider the $J-K$ circuit and suppose that initially both stages are reset ($Q_A = Q_B = 0$). The trailing edge of the first clock pulse (input pulse) will toggle flip-flop A and Q_A will change from 0 to 1. The other flip-flop will be unaffected. The second pulse will again toggle flip-flop A and make Q_A change from 1 to 0. This is the trailing edge of a pulse so that flip-flop B also toggles to give $Q_B = 1$. Thus, after two input pulses the state of the counter is $Q_A = 0$, $Q_B = 1$. A third input pulse will cause *FFA* to toggle again but the change from 0 to 1 in Q_A will have no effect on *FFB*. Now both flip-flops are set and $Q_A = Q_B = 1$.

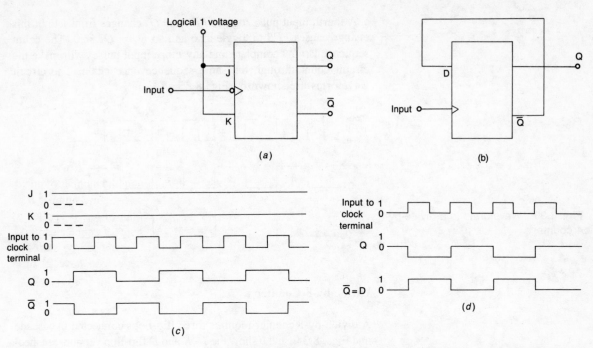

Fig. 8.31 Divide-by-2 circuits: (*a*) *J-K* flip-flop, (*b*) *D* flip-flop, (*c*) *J-K* waveforms, and (*d*) *D* waveforms

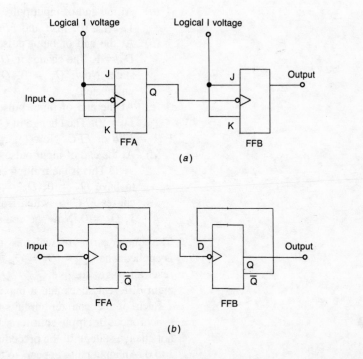

Fig. 8.32 Divide-by-4 counter: (*a*) *J-K* flip-flop, and (*b*) *D* flip-flop

A fourth input pulse toggles *FFA* and Q_A changes from 1 to 0; this change causes *FFB* to toggle also and so $Q_A = Q_B = 0$. The count sequence is now complete and any more input pulses will make the circuit count through the same sequence once again. The circuit waveforms are shown by Fig. 8.33.

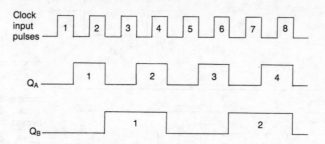

Fig. 8.33 Waveforms in a divide-by-4 counter

Divide-by-8 Counter

A divide-by-8 counter requires three flip-flops connected in cascade and Figs. 8.34*a* and *b* show the *J*−*K* and *D* flip-flop versions, respectively. This time the operation of the *D* flip-flop circuit will be described. Suppose that all three flip-flops are initially reset so that $Q_A = Q_B = Q_C = 0$ and $D_A = D_B = D_C = 1$.

(a) At the end of input pulse 1 *FFA* changes state to have $Q_A = 1$, $D_A = 0$. *FFB* and *FFC* are unaffected.

(b) At the end of input pulse 2 *FFA* changes state to $Q_A = 0$, $D_A = 1$. The change in Q_A from 1 to 0 causes *FFB* to change state. Now: $Q_A = 0$, $Q_B = 1$; $D_A = 1$, $D_B = 0$. *FFC* is unaffected.

(c) At the end of input pulse 3 *FFA* changes state to $Q_A = 1$, $D_A = 0$. The change in Q_A from 0 to 1 does not affect either *FFB* or *FFC*. Now $Q_A = Q_B = 1$, $D_A = D_B = 0$.

(d) At the end of input pulse 4 *FFA* changes state to $Q_A = 0$, $D_A = 1$. This is the trailing edge of a pulse so that *FFB* switches to have $Q_B = 0$, $D_B = 1$. The change in Q_B from 1 to 0 causes *FFC* to switch from RESET to SET and have $Q_C = 1$, $D_C = 0$. Now the counter state is $Q_A = Q_B = 0$, $Q_C = 1$.

The counter carries on with this sequence until the seventh input pulse is applied when $Q_A = Q_B = Q_C = 1$. An eighth input pulse will then reset all stages to give $Q_A = Q_B = Q_C = 0$. Thus the circuit has eight different states and a maximum count of 111 or decimal 7.

Each of the counter circuits described so far have been non-synchronous or **ripple counters**. Each flip-flop, other than *FFA*, cannot change state until the preceding flip-flop has changed state from 1 to 0. An input pulse appears to 'ripple' through the circuit and there is a cumulative delay in operation. Faster operation can be obtained

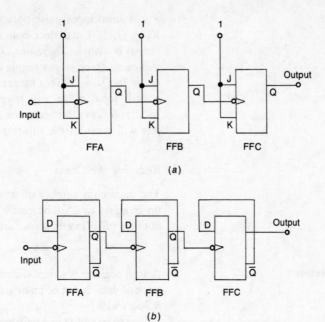

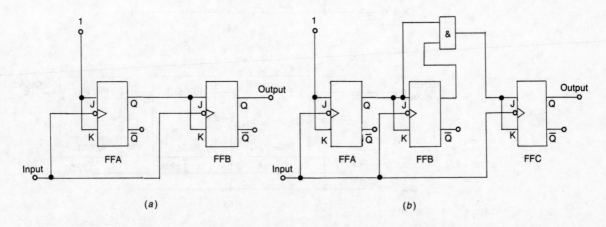

Fig. 8.34 Divide-by-8 counter: (a) J-K flip-flop, (b) D flip-flop

if all the flip-flops can be made to change state simultaneously. A *synchronous* counter has all the flip-flop clock terminals connected together and to the input terminal so that all stages change state at the same instant.

Figs. 8.35a and b respectively show synchronous divide-by-4 and divide-by-8 counters.

The operation of the divide-by-8 counter is as follows. Assuming that all three flip-flops are initially reset the trailing edge of the first input pulse toggles *FFA* so that $Q_A = J_B = K_B = 1$. The next input pulse toggles both *FFA* and *FFB* to give $Q_A = J_B = K_B = 0$, $Q_B = 1$. Since $Q_A = 0$ the output of the AND gate is 0 and so is J_C and

Fig. 8.35 Synchronous counters: (a) divide-by-4, (b) divide-by-8

K_C. A third input pulse only makes *FFA* toggle. Now $Q_A = J_B = K_B = Q_B = 1$ and since both inputs to the AND gate are now 1 its output is also 1. Therefore, $J_C = K_C = 1$. The fourth input pulse makes all three stages toggle and produces the counter state $Q_A = Q_B = 0$, $Q_C = 1$. This means that $J_B = K_B = J_C = K_C = 0$ and so a fifth input pulse will toggle *FFA* only. The operation of the counter follows this sequence until an eighth input pulse is received; this will reset all the flip-flops and clear the circuit.

Reducing the Count

The maximum number of states which an n-stage counter can take up is equal to 2^n. The count can be reduced to less than 2^n in a number of different ways that are beyond the scope of this book.

Shift Registers

A shift register is a digital circuit which can be used as a temporary store of data. It can be made using either $J-K$, or D, flip-flops, Figs. 8.36a and b.

Data to be stored in a register is applied one bit at a time (or serially) to the data input terminal. It is loaded into the register by being shifted

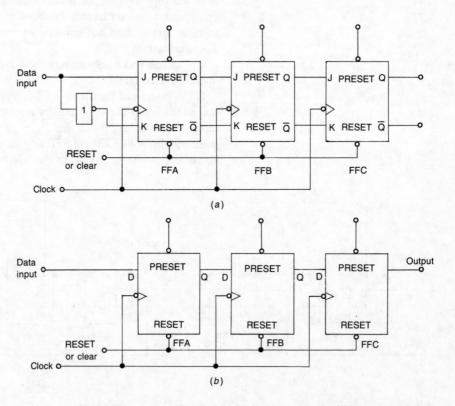

Fig. 8.36 (a) *J-K* flip-flop shift register, (b) *D* flip-flop shift registe

one place to the right at the end of each clock pulse. The number of bits of data that can be stored is equal to the number of flip-flops in a register. When the data is wanted it is moved out of the register one bit at a time by further right-shifting. This is known as a serial in – serial out (SISO) shift register. The data to be stored can also be entered into each flip-flop simultaneously, known as parallel entry; and/ or taken from each flip-flop simultaneously, known as parallel output. As a result three other types of shift register are also available; these are known as the (a) serial in – parallel out (SIPO), (b) parallel in – parallel out (PIPO), and (c) parallel in – serial out (PISO) shift registers.

Both counters and shift registers are available in the ttl and the cmos logic families. The counters are of either the synchronous or the non-synchronous kinds and may be 4-bit or 8-bit types. Any of them may be either a binary counter or a decade counter. A binary counter is the sort of counter previously described while a binary counter is a 4-bit counter that has had its maximum count reduced to 9, (0 to 9 is 10 different states), by resetting all the internal flip-flops when the count reaches 10; this takes the output of the counter to 0.

An up-down counter is able to count upwards from 0 to some maximum value, say 15, or downwards from 15 to 0. The direction of the count is determined by taking a count-up pin either high or low.

Exercises

1 Simplified Semiconductor Theory

1.1   An atom of indium has 49 electrons. how many of these are (a) in the innermost orbit, (b) in the outermost orbit?

1.2   How many electrons has a copper atom? How many of these are valence electrons? How many protons are there in its nucleus?

1.3   Arsenic has atomic number 33 and is in group V of the Periodic Table of the Elements. How many electrons are there in (a) the innermost orbit, (b) the outermost orbit?

1.4   Give two examples of a conductor, an insulator, and a semiconductor. State the effect of temperature change on the resistivity of each.

1.5   The number x of electrons allowed in a particular shell is given by $x = 2n^2$. Calculate the maximum number of electrons in each of the first three shells.

1.6   The charge of an electron is 1.602×10^{-19}C. Calculate the charge of the central core of a silicon atom.

1.7   Explain how a hole moves through a silicon crystal.

1.8   Silicon has a resistivity of 0.5-Ω-m at $27°C$. Calculate its resistivity when the temperature is $30°C$.

1.9   Explain with the aid of a sketch how silicon atoms are held together by means of covalent bonds.

1.10   Draw an n-type region with a battery connected across it. Indicate (a) the direction in which electrons move, (b) the direction in which holes move, and (c) the direction of current flow out of the battery.

1.11   For Table 1.1, tick as appropriate, *either* the donor *or* the acceptor box beneath each element.

1.12   An n-type region contains more free electrons than holes. Why, therefore, is the semiconductor electrically neutral?

1.13   An intrinsic semiconductor is doped with trivalent atoms. What charge has the resulting extrinsic material? Briefly explain your answer.

1.14   What is the polarity of the potential barrier? Should it be increased or decreased in order for a majority charge carrier current to flow? What polarity bias voltage is needed to achieve this?

1.15   A p–n junction is forward biased. Draw a sketch to show (a) the majority charge carrier current, (b) the minority charge carrier current, (c) the hole current, and (d) the battery current.

1.16   Assuming the barrier potential to be 0.6 V calculate the current flowing in Fig. 1a.

1.17   Assuming the barrier potential to be 0.62 V calculate the current flowing in Fig. 1b.

1.18   What is a depletion layer and how is it formed? Is it a region of high or of low resistivity? Is the width of a depletion layer increased or decreased by a reverse bias voltage? Will this assist in or oppose the flow of minority charge carriers across the junction?

Table 1.1

Element	Aluminium	Arsenic	Antimony	Boron	Indium
Donor					
Acceptor					

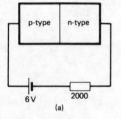

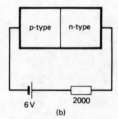

Fig. 1

1.19 Explain why a p−n junction has self-capacitance. Is this capacitance increased or decreased by an increase in the reverse bias voltage?

2 Semiconductor Diodes

2.1 Sketch a p−n junction and indicate the polarity of the barrier potential. What is its approximate value for a silicon diode? Label the anode and the cathode. Sketch the construction of a planar diode.

2.2 Two diodes, one a germanium type and the other a silicon type, have equal current ratings. If the silicon diode needs 0.70 V to conduct a current of 8 mA, what voltage must be applied to the germanium diode to get the same current flow?

2.3 The reverse saturation current of a diode is 50 nA. Is this a germanium or a silicon device? If the peak inverse voltage is 100 V estimate the breakdown voltage.

2.4 Fig. 2 shows a typical diode characteristic. Determine (*a*) its d.c. forward resistance, (*b*) its a.c. forward resistance when $V = 1.2$ V.

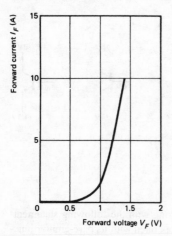

Fig. 2

2.5 A d.c. voltage of 1.1 V is applied to the diode of **2.4**. Calculate the power dissipated in the diode.

2.6 A sinusoidal signal of peak value of 1 V is applied to the ideal diode characteristic given in Fig. 3. Plot the waveform of the output current.

2.7 A diode has a maximum forward current of 10 A, a forward voltage drop of 1.3 V at a forward current of 3 A, a reverse saturation current of 1 mA, and a reverse voltage breakdown of 300 V. Plot the characteristic of the diode.

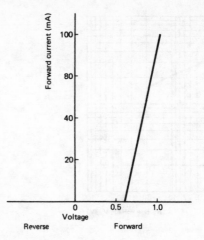

Fig. 3

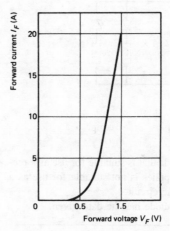

Fig. 4

2.8 For the diode characteristic of Fig. 4 calculate the ratio of the forward d.c. and a.c. resistances when the applied voltage is 0.8 V.

2.9 A Zener diode has a breakdown voltage of 9.1 V and a maximum power dissipation of 1.3 W. Calculate the maximum current the diode should pass.

2.10 Calculate the capacitance of the varactor diode whose characteristic is shown in Fig. 5 when the bias voltage is 2 V.

2.11 Fig. 4 shows the I/V characteristic of a diode. Determine the change in the diode current when the forward voltage changes from 0.7 to 0.8 V. Hence calculate the a.c. resistance of the diode. A 0.1 V peak sinusoidal voltage is applied to the diode. Plot the current waveform.

2.12 Each of the diodes shown in Fig. 6 is ideal. Calculate the battery current.

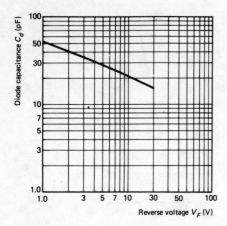

Fig. 5

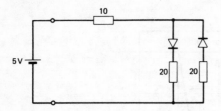

Fig. 6

2.13 Explain why a diode that is suitable for use as a rectifier of 50 Hz mains supplies is not suitable for use as a switching diode in a logic circuit.
2.14 A semiconductor diode has the data given.

Forward voltage (V)	0	0.2	0.4	0.5	0.6	0.7	0.8	0.9
Forward current (mA)	0	0	0.02	0.2	1	8	20	60

The reverse saturation current is 20 nA and the maximum reverse voltage is 50 V. Plot the static characteristic of the diode. Is this a silicon or a germanium diode? Estimate the breakdown voltage of the diode. Suggest a use for the diode.
2.15 A semiconductor diode has the data given.

Forward voltage (V)	0	0.4	0.8	1.0	1.2	1.4	1.6	1.8	2.0
Forward current (A)	0	0.03	0.06	0.25	1	6	14	28	70

At the maximum reverse voltage of 300 V the reverse saturation current is 1 μA. Plot the static characterisic of the diode

and determine (i) its d.c. forward resistance when the forward voltage is 1 V, and (ii) the a.c. resistance at the point $V = 1.4$ V. What kind of diode is this?
2.16 A Zener diode has the reverse voltage characteristic given by the data in the table.

Reverse voltage (V)	−1	−3	−5	−5.6	−5.7	−5.8	−5.9	−6.0
Reverse current (mA)	0.01	0.01	0.02	1	13	25	37.5	50

Plot the reverse characteristic of the diode. What is the breakdown voltage of the diode? Determine the a.c. resistance of the diode in its breakdown region.

3 Bipolar Transistors

3.1 An n−p−n transistor has an emitter current of 3.2 mA and a current gain h_{FB} of 0.99. Calculate the base current.
3.2 A p−n−p transistor has an emitter current of 3.2 mA and a base current of 100 μA. Calculate the collector current.
3.3 One of the transistors shown in Fig. 7 is conducting. Is it (a), (b), (c) or (d)?

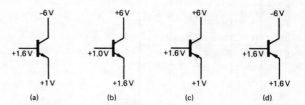

Fig. 7

3.4 Explain what is wrong with the following statement. An n−p−n transistor is operated with its base-emitter junction forward biased and its collector-base junction reverse biased. When the base potential is made more negative, the collector current is reduced in value.
3.5 Explain why the collector current of a transistor is *always* smaller than the emitter current.
3.6 A transistor has an emitter injection ratio of 0.997 and a base transmission factor of 0.996. Calculate its short-circuit current gain in the common-emitter configuration.
3.7 Draw the block diagram of an n−p−n transistor with its base-emitter junction forward biased and its collector-base junction reverse biased. Mark on the diagram the directions of (a) the base current, (b) electrons in the collector region and (c) holes in the emitter region.

3.8 Draw the circuit of a basic common-base amplifier using an n−p−n transistor. Explain how the signal voltage applied to the emitter is amplified.

3.9 The application of a signal voltage of 7.5 mV peak between the base and emitter terminals of an n−p−n transistor causes the emitter current to vary by ±0.5 mA about its d.c. value. If $h_{fb} = 0.99$ calculate the a.c. voltage developed across a 1200 ohm load resistor connected in the collector circuit. Calculate the voltage gain of the circuit.

3.10 For the n−p−n transistor shown in Fig. 8 indicate the directions of (a) the emitter, base and collector currents, (b) holes in the base region, and (c) electrons in the two batteries.

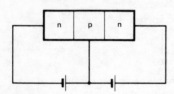

Fig. 8

3.11 A transistor has a current gain of 150 and a voltage gain of 300. Calculate if its power gain is (a) 150, (b) 45 000, (c) 45, or (d) 2.

3.12 A transistor has $h_{fe} = 350$. Calculate h_{fb}.

3.13 A transistor has a base current of 10 μA, a current gain of 90, and a collector leakage current I_{CBO} of 5 nA. Calculate its collector current.

3.14 An n−p−n transistor has $h_{fb} = 0.998$. Calculate its h_{fe} value. What would be the h_{fe} of a p−n−p transistor having the same value of h_{fb}?

3.15 A transistor has $h_{fe} = 250$, and an input resistance h_{ie} of 1200 ohms. It is connected in a circuit with a load resistor of 1000 ohms. Calculate its power gain.

3.16 An n−p−n transistor has an input resistance of 1000 ohms and it is connected to a source of e.m.f. 50 mV and impedance 1000 ohms. Calculate (a) the base current, (b) the signal base-emitter voltage.

3.17 A transistor has a current gain h_{fe} of 400. Calculate its current gain h_{fb}.

3.18 A transistor has $h_{FE} = 120$. Calculate h_{FC}.

3.19 A transistor has $h_{FB} = 0.985$. Calculate both h_{FE} and h_{FC}.

3.20 Derive from the output characteristics given in Fig. 9 the transfer characteristics for the transistor. Is the device n−p−n or p−n−p?

3.21 Fig. 10 shows the input characteristic of a transistor. Calculate its input resistance when $V_{BE} = 1$ V, 1.2 V, 1.4 V, 1.6 V and 1.8 V and then plot input resistance against base current.

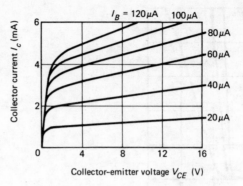

Fig. 9

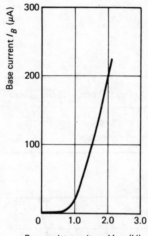

Fig. 10

3.22 A transistor has an output resistance of 15 kilohms and its operating point is $V_{CE} = 6$ V, $I_C = 2$ mA. What will be the collector current when $V_{CE} = 8$ V?

3.23 Draw a typical set of output characteristics for an n−p−n transistor and then use them to explain (a) how the collector current depends upon the base current, (b) how the collector current depends upon the collector-emitter voltage.

3.24 Fig. 11 gives the mutual characteristics of an n−p−n transistor. Determine the minimum, typical and maximum values of the mutual conductance of the transistor when the collector current is 20 mA.

3.25 Data for a transistor is given in Table 3.1. Plot curves showing how (a) the current gain and (b) the mutual conductance vary with the collector current.

3.26 The input and transfer characteristics of a transistor

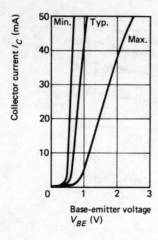

Fig. 11

Table 3.1

Base-emitter voltage (V)	0.5	0.55	0.6	0.65
Base current (μA)	0	1	12	70
Collector current (mA)	0	0.08	1.5	11.5

are given in Fig. 12. Use the characteristics to find the collector current when the base-emitter voltage is 0.7 V.

3.27 Fig. 13 shows the mutual characteristics of a transistor. (*a*) What type of transistor is it? (*b*) Calculate the mutual conductance when the base-emitter voltage is (i) 700 mV, (ii) 750 mV.

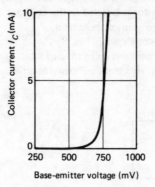

Fig. 13

3.28 For the output characteristics shown in Fig. 14 calculate the output resistance of the transistor when the collector-emitter voltage is 5 V and the base-emitter voltage is (i) 620 mV and (ii) 640 mV.

3.29 For the transistor whose characteristics are given in Fig. 13 calculate the mutual conductance when the collector-emitter voltage is 5 V and the base-emitter voltage is 620 mV.

3.30 For the transistor referred to in Fig. 14 determine the value of the collector current for each value of the base-emitter voltage when $V_{CE} = 6$ V. Then plot the mutual

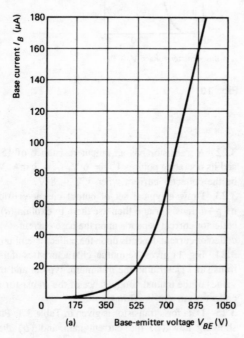

(a) Base-emitter voltage V_{BE} (V)

Fig. 12

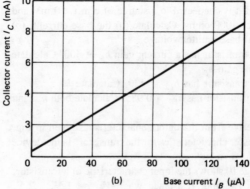

(b) Base current I_B (μA)

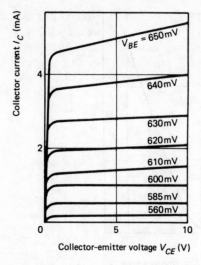

Fig. 14

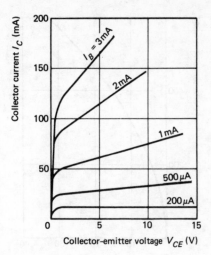

Fig. 15

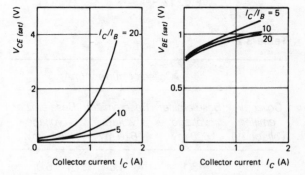

Fig. 16

characteristic of the transistor when the collector-emitter voltage is 6 V.

3.31 A transistor has the following data: (i) maximum V_{CB} = 10 V, (ii) maximum power dissipation = 1 W, (iii) current gain = 40, (iv) f_t = 20 MHz. The device is (a) a general-purpose transistor, (b) an r.f. amplifier, (c) a lower-power transistor, or (d) a high-power transistor. Give reasons for your choice.

3.32 A transistor has a maximum power dissipation of 500 mW. If the d.c. voltage applied between the collector and the emitter is 15 V calculate the maximum possible d.c. collector current.

3.33 A transistor has a f_t of 1000 MHz. Calculate its h_{fe} at 100 MHz.

3.34 Why is the maximum collector-base voltage of a transistor more important when the transistor is used as a power amplifier than when it is used as a small-signal amplifier?

3.35 List four factors that influence the efficiency of a heat sink.

3.36 Fig. 15 shows a typical set of output characteristics for an n–p–n transistor. If the transistor is to be used as a switch with a collector supply voltage of 15 V and a load of 150 ohms draw a load line and indicate the regions in which the transistor is (a) ON and (b) OFF.

3.37 Fig. 16 shows a typical set of curves of (a) $V_{CE(sat)}$ and (b) $V_{BE(sat)}$ plotted against collector current for a transistor. Calculate $V_{CE(sat)}$ and $V_{BE(sat)}$ for I_C = 1 A and I_B = 50 mA.

3.38 Draw a typical set of output characteristics for an n–p–n transistor and on them mark the ON and OFF regions. Explain why little power is dissipated in the transistor whilst it is in either the ON or the OFF state.

3.39 In a common-emitter amplifier the current gain of the transistor is 120, the input resistance of the transistor is 3 kΩ and the collector load resistance is 2 kΩ. Determine the voltage and power gains of the amplifier.

3.40 Figs. 17a and b show, respectively, the transfer and mutual characteristics of a transistor. Determine (a) the current gain h_{fe}, (b) the mutual conductance g_m, and (c) the input resistance h_{ie} of the device.

3.41 The data given in Table 3.2 refer to a transistor in the common-emitter configuration.

Use the data to plot the output characteristics for V_{BE} = 600 mV, 610 mV and 620 mV. Use the characteristics to determine: (a) the output resistance of the transistor for V_{BE} = 610 mV, (b) the mutual conductance for V_{CE} = 6 V.

3.42 The data given in Table 3.3 refer to a transistor in the common-emitter configuration.

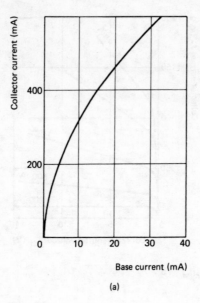

Fig. 17

(a)

(b)

Table 3.2

| Collector-emitter voltage (V) | Collector current (mA) | | |
	Base-emitter voltage 600 mV	Base-emitter voltage 610 mV	Base-emitter voltage 620 mV
1	3.1	4.6	6.0
3	3.5	5.1	6.6
5	3.9	5.6	7.2
7	4.3	6.1	7.8
9	4.7	6.6	8.4

Table 3.3

| Collector-emitter voltage (V) | Collector current (mA) | | |
	Base current $-10\,\mu A$	Base current $-20\,\mu A$	Base current $-30\,\mu A$
-2	-2.9	-4.4	-5.9
-4	-3.3	-4.9	-6.4
-6	-3.7	-5.4	-7.0
-8	-4.1	-5.9	-7.6
-10	-4.5	-6.4	-8.2

Draw the output characteristic for I_B = -10, -20, -30 μA. Use the characteristics to determine: (a) the output resistance of the transistor for I_B = -20 μA, (b) the current gain for V_{CE} = -7 V.

3.43 Table 3.4 gives values of the collector current-collector voltage for a series of base current values in a transistor in the common-emitter configuration. Plot these characteristics and hence find (i) the current gain when the collector voltage is 6 V, (ii) the output resistance for a base current of 45 μA.

Table 3.4

| Collector-emitter voltage (V) | Collector current (mA) | | | |
	Base current $25\,\mu A$	Base current $45\,\mu A$	Base current $65\,\mu A$	Base current $85\,\mu A$
3	0.91	1.59	2.25	3.00
5	0.92	1.69	2.45	3.20
7	0.96	1.84	2.65	3.50
9	0.99	2.04	2.95	4.00

4 Field-effect Transistors

4.1 Explain how a depletion layer is formed in the channel of a jfet by the applied drain-source voltage and how the channel resistance varies with this voltage for small voltages. What effect stops this happening at higher voltages?

4.2 Label each part of the jfet shown in Fig. 18 and say whether it is a p-channel or an n-channel device.

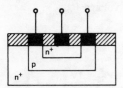

Fig. 18

4.3 A jfet has a mutual conductance of 3 mS. A signal of 1.5 V peak is applied between the gate and the source terminals. Calculate the peak drain signal current that flows.

4.4 A jfet has an output resistance of 50 kΩ. When a signal of 1.5 V peak is applied to the transistor the drain current varies by ±2 mA about its steady (quiescent) value. Calculate the mutual conductance of the transistor.

4.5 When the gate-source voltage of a jfet is held at a constant value it is found that a change in the drain-source voltage of 2 V produces a change in the drain current of 0.5 mA. Calculate the output resistance of the fet.

4.6 Explain how the symbols for the four types of mosfet indicate (i) whether the device is p-type or n-type channel, (ii) whether drain current will flow in the absence of a gate-source voltage.

4.7 Explain the effects on the performance of a mosfet of an increase in the temperature of the device.

4.8 Explain the action of a p-channel enhancement-mode mosfet.

4.9 Fig. 19 shows the mutual and drain characteristics of a fet. Calculate, using both characteristics, the mutual conductance when the gate-source voltage is 0.4 V.

4.10 For the fet quoted in **4.9** calculate its output resistance when $V_{GS} = -0.4$ V.

4.11 For the characteristics shown in Fig. 20 calculate the gate-source voltage needed to give a d.c. drain current of 8 mA. If the drain-source voltage is 8 V, estimate the d.c. resistance of the fet for this value of V_{GS}.

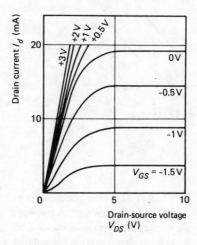

Fig. 20

4.12 Explain why thermal runaway is not a problem with a fet.

4.13 The drain-source voltage of a jfet is increased from 6 V to 7 V. The resulting increase in the drain current is 0.1 mA. Calculate the output resistance of the fet. Assume that there is zero change in the value of the gate-source voltage.

4.14 A depletion-mode mosfet has the data given in Table 4.1. Plot the mutual characteristic and hence determine the mutual conductance of the device when the gate-source voltage is 1.2 V.

Table 4.1

Drain current (mA)	7.0	5.5	4.0	2.5	1.7	0.5	0
Gate-source voltage (V)	0	0.5	1.0	1.5	2.0	3.0	4.0

4.15 In a fet amplifier circuit, $V_{gs} = 1.5$ V, $E_s = 1$ V, $R_s = 2500$ ohms and $R_L = 3000$ ohms. If the mutual conductance g_m of the fet is 2 mS calculate the a.c. voltage developed across R_L.

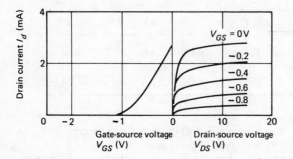

Fig. 19

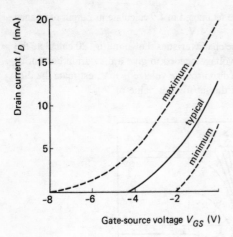

Fig. 21

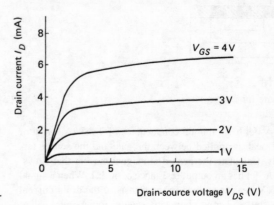

Fig. 22

4.20 Use the data given in Table 4.2 to plot the mutual characteristic of the fet for $V_{DS} = 8$ V.

4.21 Fig. 22 shows the drain characteristics of an n-channel enhancement-mode mosfet which is to be used as a switch. Mark the characteristics with the ON and OFF regions of the device. Estimate the saturation voltage $V_{DS(SAT)}$.

4.16 Explain how the channel depletion region of a p-channel jfet increases in width as the drain-source voltage is increased. Make clear whether this voltage increases from zero volts to a positive or a negative value. What polarity must the gate-source voltage be to still further increase the width of the depletion region?

4.17 The maximum gate current $I_{G(max)}$ for a particular type of jfet is 200 nA. Calculate its input resistance when $V_{GS} = 2$ V.

4.18 Fig. 21 shows the maximum, typical and minimum mutual characteristics of an n-channel jfet. Determine the maximum, typical and minimum value of the mutual conductance g_m of the fet.

4.19 The drain characteristics of a fet are given by the data of Table 4.2. Plot the characteristics and state which type of fet it is. Calculate the values of the mutual conductance g_m and the drain-source resistance r_{ds} when $V_{DS} = 6$ V.

4.22 When a fet is ON its drain current is 8 mA. If $V_{DS(SAT)} = 0.8$ V calculate the ON resistance of the fet.

4.23 What is meant by the active region of a fet characteristic? Why does a fet dissipate more power when it is in this region than when it is in either its ON or its OFF region?

4.24 The drain characteristics of a fet are given in Table 4.3. Plot the characteristics and determine the drain-source resistance from the characteristic for $V_{GS} = 0.5$ V.

Table 4.3

Drain current I_D (mA)					
Drain-source voltage V_{DS}(V)	Gate-source voltage V_{GS}				
	1 V	0.5 V	0 V	–0.5 V	–1 V
10	4.00	3.19	2.38	1.57	0.76
20	4.02	3.21	2.40	1.59	0.78
30	4.04	3.23	2.43	1.61	0.80

Use the curves to find the mutual conductance for $V_{DS} = 20$ V. What type of fet is this?

4.25 An n-channel junction fet has the data given in Table 4.4. Plot the drain and mutual characteristics and use them

Table 4.2

Drain current I_D(mA)						
Drain-source voltage V_{DS}(V)	Gate-source voltage V_{GS}(V)					
	–3	–2	–1	0	+0.5	+1
2	0.8	2.5	5.0	7.7	8.6	11.8
4	0.8	3.0	5.8	8.6	10.5	13.0
8	0.8	3.1	5.9	9.0	11.4	13.5
20	0.8	3.2	6.0	9.2	11.8	14.0

Table 4.4

Drain-source voltage V_{DS}(V)	Drain current (mA)			
	Gate-source voltage V_{GS}			
	0 V	–0.5 V	–1.0 V	–1.5 V
10	2.25	1.35	0.7	0.3
20	2.29	1.38	0.73	0.33
30	2.32	1.41	0.75	0.35

to determine the mutual conductance of the device. Find also the drain-source resistance.

5 Integrated Circuits

5.1 Show that the resistance/□ of a silicon chip layer is given by $R = \rho/d$ Ω/□, where ρ is the resistivity of the silicon and d is the thickness of the layer.

A silicon layer has a resistance of 180 Ω/□. Calculate the resistance of a strip that is 1.5 mil wide and 30 mil in length.

5.2 The resistivity of a silicon layer of sides a and b, where $a = b$, is 120 Ω/□. What will it be if (a) a is doubled and b is unchanged, (b) both a and b are doubled, (c) a is unchanged and b is doubled?

5.3 Calculate the resistance of the IC resistor shown in Fig. 23 if (a) $R = 120$ Ω/□ and (b) $R = 200$ Ω/□.

5.4 Calculate the resistance of the IC resistor shown in Fig. 24 if $R = 250$ Ω/□. Suggest another method of obtaining the same resistance value.

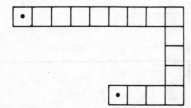

Fig. 23

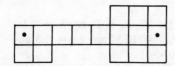

Fig. 24

5.5 An IC resistor is to be designed using material having a resistivity of 150 Ω/□. Draw a possible layout if the required resistance is (a) 225 Ω and (b) 375 Ω.

5.6 The capacitance of a junction capacitor in an IC is 0.25 pF/mil². Calculate the chip area needed to provide a capacitor of 50 pF.

5.7 Why are high values of resistance and capacitance not fabricated in an IC chip? How are any such components that are needed provided?

5.8 Explain why an integrated p—n—p transistor cannot be made using the same technique as employed to make an n—p—n transistor.

5.9 Draw the integrated circuit version of the circuit given in Fig. 25.

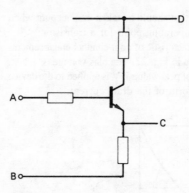

Fig. 25

5.10 Very often a required resistance value is obtained in a silicon chip by means of a suitably biased bipolar or field-effect transistor. Show how each transistor can be connected to act as a resistance.

5.11 Give four advantages of integrated circuits over their discrete component versions.

5.12 Describe, using appropriate sketches, how either (i) an enhancement-type mosfet or (ii) a bipolar transistor can be fabricated in integrated circuit form.

5.13 Explain, with sketches, how: (i) a capacitor, (ii) a resistor, (iii) a diode can be formed on a silicon chip. Describe any method which can be used to isolate electrically each component formed within a silicon chip.

5.14 Explain the meaning of the following when applied to integrated circuits: (i) planar process, (ii) diffusion, (iii) epitaxial layer, (iv) metallization.

6 Small-signal Audio-frequency Amplifiers

6.1 Fig. 26 shows how the d.c. current gain h_{FE} of a transistor varies with the collector current I_C. If the maximum

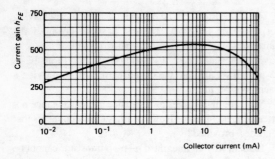

Fig. 26

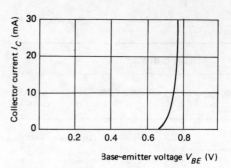

Fig. 28

gain is required determine the value of I_C that should be chosen.

6.2 List the factors that should be taken into account when choosing a suitable operating point for a transistor.

6.3 The mutual characteristic of an n-channel enhancement-mode mosfet is shown in Fig. 27. The bias voltage is +2 V. If a sinusoidal signal of peak value 1 V is applied to the device determine the waveform of the drain current.

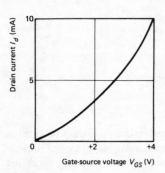

Fig. 27

6.4 Explain, with the aid of a typical mutual characteristic, why Class B or Class C bias cannot be used with a single-ended resistance-loaded amplifier.

6.5 Fig. 28 shows a typical mutual characteristic for a bipolar transistor. Determine suitable base-emitter bias voltages for (a) Class A, (b) Class B, and (c) Class C bias.

6.6 Explain why d.c. stabilization of a fet is necessary even though thermal runaway is not a problem. Hence, explain the disadvantage of the circuit given by Fig. 29a.

6.7 In Fig. 30a, $V_{DD} = 12$ V, $R_3 = 3$ kΩ and $V_{DS} = 6$ V. Calculate the drain current. If $R_1 = R_2$ calculate V_{GS} also.

6.8 In the circuit of Fig. 29b, $R_1 = 470$ kΩ, $R_2 = 3$ kΩ and $R_3 = 1.2$ kΩ. Calculate the gate-source bias voltage if the drain current is 1.5 mA.

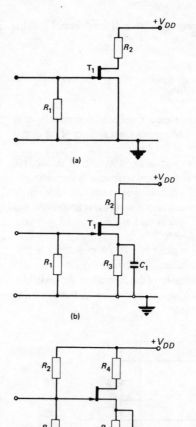

Fig. 29

6.9 In Fig. 29c, $R_2 = 150$ kΩ, $R_1 = 22$ kΩ, $R_3 = 2$ kΩ and $R_4 = 3.8$ kΩ. If $V_{DD} = 15$ V and $I_D = 1.5$ mA calculate (a) V_{DS} and (b) V_{GS}.

6.10 In Fig. 30b $R_1 = 300$ kΩ and $R_2 = 4.7$ kΩ, if V_{DS}

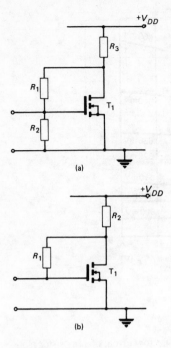

(a)

(b)

Fig. 30

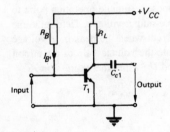

Fig. 31

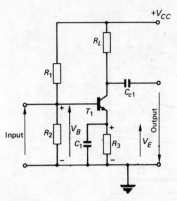

Fig. 32

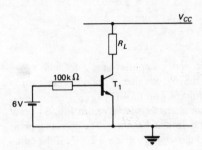

Fig. 33

6.11 In the circuit of Fig. 31, $V_{CC} = 6$ V and $R_B = 470$ kΩ. If $V_{BE} = 0.61$ V, calculate the base current I_B.

6.12 In Fig. 32 the collector-to-earth voltage is 9 V, $R_L = 3$ kΩ and $I_C = 2$ mA. Calculate the supply voltage V_{CC}. If the emitter resistor is 1 kΩ calculate V_E.

6.13 In Fig. 32 $V_{CC} = 12$ V, the collector-to-earth voltage is 6 V and the power dissipated in R_L is 6 mW. Calculate (a) R_L and (b) I_C.

6.14 In Fig. 32 $R_3 = 1.2$ kΩ and $I_C = 1.8$ mA. If $h_{FE} = 100$ and $V_{BE} = 0.62$ V calculate (a) I_B and (b) the voltage across R_2.

6.15 The transistor used in the circuit of Fig. 33 has $V_{BE} = 0.63$ V and $h_{FE} = 85$. Calculate I_C.

6.16 In Fig. 32 $V_{CC} = 12$ V and $I_C = 2$ mA. If 1/10th of the supply voltage appears across R_3 calculate R_3. If $V_{CE} = V_{CC}/2$ calculate R_L. If $h_{FE} = 100$ calculate I_B. If $I_{R2} = 10I_B$ calculate R_1 and R_2. $V_{BE} = 0.65$ V.

6.17 For the circuit of **6.16**, calculate the d.c. input power. Also find the collector dissipation for zero signal conditions.

6.18 A transistor has $h_{FE} = 120$ and $I_{CBO} = 20$ nA. Calculate its collector current when the base current is 20 μA.

6.19 In the circuit of Fig. 32 $V_{CC} = 12$ V, $R_1 = 33$ kΩ, $R_2 = 10$ kΩ and $R_3 = 1.2$ kΩ. If $I_C = 1.75$ mA calculate the V_{BE} bias voltage of the transistor.

6.20 The bias circuit of Fig. 32 is designed with the h_{FE} value assumed to be the nominal value of 100. One circuit is constructed using this type of transistor where the h_{FE} value is the minimum of 70. Explain how the circuit operates to ensure that the collector current is very nearly equal to the designed-for value.

6.21 The signal voltage applied to the base of a transistor with $g_m = 40$ mS has a peak value of 0.1 V. Calculate the peak value of the a.c. component of the collector current. If the collector load resistance is 4.7 kΩ determine the output voltage of the circuit and the voltage gain.

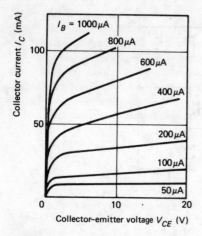

Fig. 34

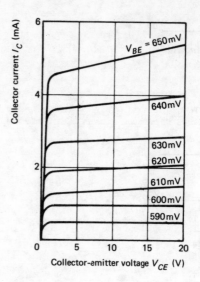

Fig. 35

6.22 An audio-frequency amplifier uses a fet with $r_{ds} = 10$ kΩ and $g_m = 5$ mS. What value of drain load resistor is needed to give a voltage gain of 40?

6.23 On the output characteristics given in Fig. 34 draw the load line for a d.c. load of 400 ohms. The operating point is $I_B = 150$ μA and the supply voltage is 20 V. If the emitter resistance is 100 ohms calculate V_E, V_{CE} and the collector-to-earth voltage. Determine the peak-to-peak output voltage when a sinusoidal voltage varies the base current by ±50 μA.

6.24 Fig. 35 shows the collector current of a transistor plotted against collector-emitter voltage for various values of base-emitter voltage. The transistor is used in an amplifier (Fig. 32) with $V_{CC} = 20$ V, $R_L = 3.5$ kΩ and $R_3 = 500$ Ω. Draw the load line and choose a suitable operating point to give the maximum possible output voltage. Determine the peak-to-peak collector current when the peak base voltage change is 25 mV. Calculate the voltage gain of the circuit (a) from the load line, and (b) using the expression $A_v = g_m R_L$.

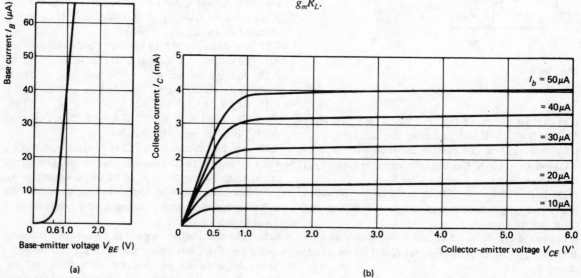

(a)

(b)

Fig. 36

6.25 Figs 36*a* and *b* show, respectively, the input and output characteristics of a transistor. The transistor is used in a single-stage amplifier with $V_{CC} = 6$ V, $R_L = 1800$ ohms and emitter resistance $= 200$ ohms. Draw the load line and mark the operating point for a base bias current of 20 μA. Determine the required bias voltage V_{BE}. Calculate the ratio $\delta I_C/\delta V_{BE}$.

6.26 Fig. 37 shows both the mutual and drain characteristics of an n-channel jfet. If $V_{DD} = 20$ V draw the load line for $R_L = 2000$ ohms on the drain characteristic and select the operating point $V_{GS} = -2$ V. A signal voltage varies V_{GS} between the limits -1 V and -3 V. Determine from both sets of characteristics the mutual conductance of the device. Calculate the voltage gain (*a*) from the load line and (*b*) using the expression $A_v = g_m R_L$.

6.27 Fig. 38 shows a transistor output characteristic with a load line drawn on it. Determine the load to which this relates. Calculate the maximum peak-to-peak output voltage and current if the operating point is (*a*) $I_B = 1$ mA, (*b*) $I_B = 3$ mA and (*c*) $I_B = 5$ mA. Comment on the results.

6.28 For Fig. 38 calculate the d.c. power taken from the supply and the collector dissipation under no-signal conditions. Assume the base bias current I_B to be 3 mA.

7 Power Supplies

7.1 In the circuit of Fig. 39 the voltage across the secondary winding is 22 V. What should be the peak inverse voltage of each diode? What is the value of the voltage V_S when the current in the 150 Ω load is 50 mA? Assume that 0.5 V are dropped across the conducting diode.

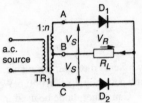

Fig. 39

7.2 The input transformer of a full-wave rectifier (Fig. 39) has a turns ratio of 9.58:1. The r.m.s. voltage at the secondary is 24 V. Calculate (*a*) the r.m.s. input voltage, (*b*) the peak current flowing in the 200 Ω load, and (*c*) the d.c. current in the 200 Ω load.

7.3 Draw the circuit of a half-wave rectifier circuit. If the voltage across the secondary winding of the transformer is 60 V what is the peak inverse voltage of the diode when the reservoir capacitor is (*a*) connected, (*b*) disconnected?

7.4 The no-load output voltage of a rectifier circuit is 24 V. When the full-load current is taken the output voltage falls to 23.4 V. Calculate the percentage regulation of the circuit.

7.5 Fig. 40 shows the circuit of a full-wave rectifier circuit. Draw sketches to show the expected waveforms (*a*) at

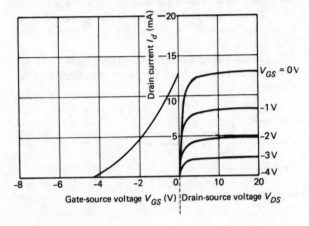

Fig. 37

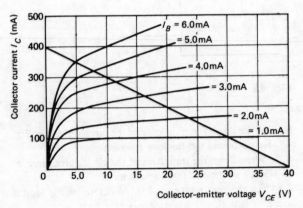

Fig. 38

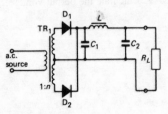

Fig. 40

the primary winding of the transformer, (b) at the secondary winding of the transformer, (c) at the junction of C_1 and L_1, and (d) across the load.

7.6 Draw the circuit of a half-wave rectifier with a capacitor input LC filter. If such a circuit has a no-load output voltage of 100 V and a regulation of 0.94% calculate the output voltage when the full load current is taken.

7.7 The circuit shown in Fig. 41 is to be used to produce 12 V output voltage at a current of 120 mA. The input voltage may vary between 14 V and 20 V. Calculate the necessary value of the series resistor R_s if the diode minimum current is 5 mA.

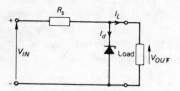

Fig. 41

7.8 In the circuit of Fig. 41 two Zener diodes are available. One of the diodes has a maximum power dissipation of 0.6 W and the other dissipates 1.2 W. Can either diode be used in the circuit?

7.9 A 24 V stabilized voltage is to be obtained from a 30 V d.c. supply. A 24 V, 3 W Zener diode is to be used. Calculate the required value for the series resistor.

7.10 A Zener diode stabilizing circuit has an input voltage of 18 V and a diode current of 8 mA to give 10 V across the load of 1200 ohms. Calculate the value of the series resistor and the diode current when the load resistance is 1000 ohms.

7.11 A 14.2 V Zener diode has a maximum power dissipation of 1.5 W. Calculate the maximum current that the diode may conduct.

8 Digital Circuits

8.1 In the circuit given in Fig. 42 the load resistor R is 1000 Ω. The voltage applied between terminals 1 and 2 makes 1 6 V positive with respect to 2. When conducting, the diode has a voltage drop of 0.65 V. Calculate the output voltage.

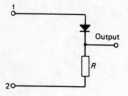

Fig. 42

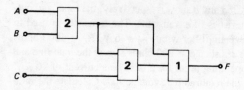

Fig. 43

8.2 When A = B = 1 and C = 0 find the output F of the circuit shown in Fig. 43.

8.3 The Boolean expression for a circuit is $F = ABCDE$. Use a truth table to show that the output of the circuit will be at logical 0 whenever $C = 0$ regardless of the values of the other inputs.

8.4 The Boolean expression for a circuit is $F = A + B + C + D + E$. Show that the output of the circuit will be at logical 1 whenever $C = 1$ regardless of the values of the other inputs.

8.5 The waveforms shown in Fig. 45 are applied to the circuit given in Fig. 44. Draw the output waveform F of the circuit.

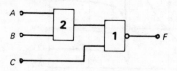

Fig. 44

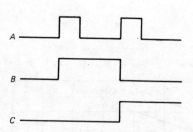

Fig. 45

8.6 Write down the truth table of the circuit given in Fig. 43. Hence obtain the Boolean equation.

8.7 Write down the truth table of the circuit given in Fig. 44. Hence obtain the Boolean equation.

8.8 For the circuit given in Fig. 46 determine the logical value of B if F = 1 when A = 1.

8.9 Write down (a) the truth table and (b) the Boolean expression describing Fig. 46.

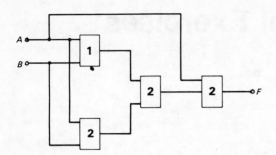

Fig. 46

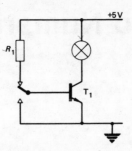

Fig. 47

8.10 The Boolean expression for a logic circuit is $F = A.B.C.D$. Show how the function can be implemented using (*a*) one gate and (*b*) two gates.

8.11 The waveforms shown in Fig. 45 are applied to Fig. 43. Draw the output waveform.

8.12 Draw circuits to perform the logical functions (*a*) $F = (A + B + C)(D + E)$ (*b*) $F = A.B.C + D(B + C)$.

8.13 The voltage table for a logic circuit is given in Table 8.1. What logical function is performed if (*a*) positive and (*b*) negative logic is employed?

Table 8.1

A	+5 V	+5 V	0 V	0 V
B	+5 V	0 V	+5 V	0 V
F	+5 V	+5 V	+5 V	0 V

8.14 For the circuit shown in Fig. 47 calculate the power dissipated in the lamp when it indicates (*a*) logical 0, (*b*) logical 1. Assume the saturation voltage $V_{CE(SAT)}$ of the transistor to be 0.2 V. The lamp's ON resistance is 250 Ω.

8.15 A circuit has its operation controlled by three switches, *A*, *B* and *C*. The circuit is required to be ON whenever switch *A*, or both *B* and *C*, are operated, or ON. Write down the truth table for this logical operation and from it derive the minimal Boolean expression describing the operation. Implement the circuit using either NAND or NOR gates only.

8.16 Draw the circuit of a divide-by-8 counter using (*a*) synchronous and (*b*) non-synchronous techniques. Describe the operation of both circuits.

8.17 Explain, with the aid of truth tables, the difference between a $S-R$ and $J-K$ flip-flop. Show how the $S-R$ flip-flop can be made using four NAND gates and how clocked operation can be arranged.

8.18 $J-K$ flip-flops are of either the master-slave or the edge-triggered types. Explain the basic differences between them.

8.19 Draw the circuit of a shift register that employs three *D* flip-flops. Briefly explain the action of the circuit when the input data to be stored is 101.

8.20 The Boolean expression $AB + \bar{B}C$ is to be implemented. Draw the circuit using (*a*) NAND gates, (*b*) NOR gates only.

8.21 Simplify the following expressions using a Karnaugh map

(i) $F = ABC + B\bar{C} + \bar{A}\bar{B}\bar{C}$

(ii) $F = ABC + \bar{A}BC + A\bar{C} + B$

(iii) $F = \bar{A} + BC + AB\bar{C} + A\bar{B}C + B\bar{C} + \bar{A}B$

Answers to Numerical Exercises

1.1	2, 3		**3.17**	0.9975
1.2	29, 1, 29		**3.18**	121
1.3	2, 5		**3.19**	65.7, 66.7
1.5	2, 8, 18		**3.20**	n-p-n
1.6	6.408×10^{-19} C		**3.22**	2.133 mA
1.8	0.402 Ω-m		**3.24**	33.3 mS, 154 mS, 200 mS
1.13	zero, decreased, positive on p-type		**3.26**	4.6 mA
1.16	2.7 mA		**3.27**	n-p-n, 30 mS, 85 mS
1.17	0 mA		**3.28**	59 kΩ, 10 kΩ
1.18	high, increased, assist		**3.29**	78 mS
1.19	decreased		**3.31**	(c)
			3.32	33.3 mA
			3.37	1.29 V, 0.93
2.1	0.6 V		**3.39**	80, 9600
2.2	0.3 V			
2.3	silicon, 120 V		**4.3**	4.5 mA
2.4	0.27 V, 0.044 Ω		**4.4**	1.33 mS
2.5	2.75 W		**4.5**	40 kΩ
2.8	4.8		**4.9**	3.5 mS
2.9	143 mA		**4.10**	40 kΩ
2.10	40 pF		**4.11**	-1.1 V, very high
2.11	0.021 Ω		**4.13**	10 kΩ
2.12	160 mA or 147 mA		**4.14**	3 mS
2.14	silicon, 65 V		**4.15**	6 V
2.15	4 Ω, 0.03 Ω, power		**4.16**	positive
2.16	5.6 V, 8 Ω		**4.17**	10 MΩ
			4.18	4.25 mS, 4 mS, 3.8 mS
			4.19	n-channel dep. type mosfet, 2.8 mS, 40 kΩ
3.1	32 μA		**4.21**	1 V to 2.5 V depending on load
3.2	3.1 mA		**4.22**	100 Ω
3.3	(c)		**4.24**	500 kΩ, n-channel dep. type mosfet
3.6	142		**4.25**	1.05 mS, 500 kΩ
3.9	594 mV, 79.2			
3.11	45 000		**5.1**	3600 Ω
3.12	0.9972		**5.2**	240 Ω/□ , 120 Ω/□ , 60 Ω/□
3.13	0.9 mA		**5.3**	1920 Ω, 3200 Ω
3.14	499, 499		**5.4**	1250 Ω
3.15	52.08×10^3		**5.6**	200 mil^2
3.16	25 μA, 25 mV			

6.1 5 mA

6.5 0.7, 0.6, −1 V

6.7 2 mA, 3 V

6.9 6.3 V, −1 V

6.10 5 V

6.11 11.5 μA

6.12 15 V, 2 V

6.13 6 kΩ, 1 mA

6.14 18 μA, 2.78 V

6.15 4.56 mA

6.16 600 Ω, 2400 Ω, 20 μA, 46.1 kΩ, 9.25 kΩ

6.17 24 mW, 12 mW

6.18 2.4 mA

6.19 0.69 V

6.21 4 mA, 18.8 V, 188

6.22 40 kΩ

6.23 2 V, 10 V, 12 V, 5.5 V

6.24 625 mV, 10.5 V, 3.7 mA, 266, 259

6.25 0.83 V, 33 mS

6.26 3 mS, 5.5, 6

6.27 100 Ω

6.28 3.9 W

7.1 44 V, 8 V

7.2 230 V, 170 mA, 108 mA

7.3 120 V, 60 V

7.4 2.5%

7.6 99.06 V

7.7 48 Ω

7.8 yes

7.9 48 Ω minimum

7.10 490 Ω, 6.33 mA

7.11 105.6 mA

8.1 5.35 V

8.2 1

8.6 F = AB

8.7 F = $\bar{A}$C + $\bar{B}$C

8.8 1

8.9 F = AB

8.13 OR, AND

8.14 0 W, 92.16 mW

8.21 AB + B$\bar{C}$, $\bar{A}\bar{C}$, B + A$\bar{C}$, 1

Index